Level A

From Phonics to Reading

Wiley Blevins

From Phonics to Reading

Douglas Fisher, Ph.D.
Senior Series Reviewer
Professor of Education
San Diego State University
San Diego, CA

Reviewers

The publisher wishes to thank for their comments and suggestions the following teachers
and administrators, who read portions of the series prior to publication.

Mindy Jo Acton
Third Grade Teacher
Barnesville Elementary
Barnesville, OH

Kathy W. Dames Ed.D.
The Intellectual Child LLC
Flossmoor, IL

Jennifer L. Jones
First Grade Teacher
Resurrection Catholic School
Lakeland, FL

Erin Kent
Remediation Specialist, K-6
Montgomery County Intermediate Unit
Norristown, PA

Nancy Osterreich
Director of Grants and School Improvement
Cicero School District 99
Cicero, IL

Luz Baeza Palomares
General Education Teacher
Discovery Charter School
Chula Vista, CA

Colleen Stahl
Academic Coach
Neshaminy School District
Langhorne, PA

Cover Series Design: Silver Linings Studios; **Cover Illustration:** Russell Benfanti; **Illustration Credits:** Bernard Adnet, Dan Andreasen, Gail Armstrong, Gene Baretta, Constanza Basaluzzo, Nathalie Beauvois, Shirley Beckes, Russell Benfanti, Ron Berg, Tim Bowers, Robin Boyer, Scott Burroughs, Andy Catlin, Holli Conger, Martina Crepilja, Steliyana Doneva, Peter Francis, Claudine Gevry, Patrick Gnan, Bob Holt, Valerie Jaskina, Katie Kath, Tammie Lyon, Dan McGeehan, Bob McMahon, Bruce McPherson, Josh Nash, Alejandro O'Kif, Bob Ostrom, Debbie Palen, Nomar Perez, Jose Ramos, Andrew Roberts, Drew Rose, Blythe Russo, Ken Spengler, Margaret Spengler, Ralph Voltz, Anne Wertheim, Kathy Wilburn, Donald Wu, Amy Wummer, Jennifer Zivion.

William H. Sadlier, Inc.
9 Pine Street
New York, NY 10005-4700

Printed in the United States of America.
ISBN: 978-1-4217-1541-4
1 2 3 4 5 6 7 8 9 10 WEBC 23 22 21 20 19

Contents

Dear Family,

Home Connection

In this unit, your child will learn about words that contain short vowels and single consonants. He or she will learn to read words with the short **a**, short **i**, short **o**, short **u**, and short **e** sounds, such as **nap**; **hid**; **mop**; **hug**; and **bed**.

Read Connected Text

For each week's lesson, your child will read a Take-Home Book that focuses on the lesson skills. At week's end, the book will be sent home with your child. Read the book to your child, or read it aloud together, pointing to each word as you say it. Multiple readings will give your child practice with the lesson skills.

Practice with the Take-Home Book

Ask your child to point to words in the story that include short vowels with single consonant spelling.

Have your child tell you about the book in one sentence. Write what your child says and read the description aloud together.

Lesson Skills and Take-Home Books

Lesson 1 Short **a**: "What Do We Like?"
Lesson 2 Short **i**: "What Is It?"
Lesson 3 Short **o**: "Frog"
Lesson 4 Short **u**: "Little Bugs, Big Bugs"
Lesson 5 Short **e**: "Birds and Their Nests"

Extend the Learning

With your child, look for words with short vowels with single consonants in books, signs, magazine covers, etc. Keep a notebook of words you discover.

Challenge your child to identify objects in your home or other locations that have a short vowel sound. For example, "I spy a mat."

 Visit SadlierConnect.com for Student & Family Resources.

Apreciada familia:

En esta unidad, su niño(a) aprenderá acerca de palabras con vocales con sonidos cortos y consonantes sencillas. Aprenderá a leer palabras con sonido corto de la **a**, de la **i**, de la **o**, de la **u** y de la **e**, como **nap**; **hid**; **mop**; **hug** y **bed**.

Leyendo la historieta en el Take-Home Book

Para cada lección de la semana su niño(a) leerá un cuadernillo de historietas, Take-Home Book, que se enfoca en las destrezas de la lección. Al final de cada semana su niño(a) llevará el cuadernillo a la casa. Lea la historieta a su niño(a) o leánla en voz alta juntos, señalando cada palabra al decirla. Leer varias veces ayudará a su niño(a) a practicar las destrezas de la lección.

Practicando con el Take-Home Book

Pida a su niño(a) señalar palabras en la historieta con vocales con sonido corto y consonantes sencillas para esa lección. Luego pídale que resuma la historieta en una frase. Escriba lo que dice su niño(a) y lean juntos lo que escribió.

Lesson Skills and Take-Home Books

Lesson 1 Short **a**: "What Do We Like?"
Lesson 2 Short **i**: "What Is It?"
Lesson 3 Short **o**: "Frog"
Lesson 4 Short **u**: "Little Bugs, Big Bugs"
Lesson 5 Short **e**: "Birds and Their Nests"

Ampliando el aprendizaje

Con su niño(a) busque palabras con vocales con sonidos cortos y consonantes sencillas en libros, letreros, portadas de revistas, etc. Haga una libreta con palabras que descubran juntos. Rete a su niño(a) a identificar, ya sea en su casa o en otros lugares, objetos con vocales con el sonido corto. Por ejemplo: "I spy a mat."

 Visite **SadlierConnect.com** **para recursos para el estudiante y la familia.**

Learn and Blend

Directions: Listen and join in.

a…a…a…
Bite that apple!

Short a

a

Blend It

Directions: Chorally read the words.

1. at	bat	fat	fan	pan	ran
2. mat	man	map	bat	bag	bad
3. ham	nap	back	tap	hat	sad

4. The cat sat.

5. The cat sat on a mat.

6. cats   caps   mats   maps   pans   fans

Daily Practice

Directions: Do one activity each day. Then check the box.

☐ **Build Fluency** Read the words each day by yourself and to a partner.

☐ **Mark It** Circle all the words with short a.

☐ **Spell It** Have a partner say each word. Write the word. Check your answer.

☐ **Write About It** Use the words to create a story. Draw a box around the words from the list that you used.

Read-Spell-Write

Directions: Write each word two times. Say each letter as you write it.

1. the ___the the___

2. like ___like like___

3. play ___play play___

4. my ___my my___

Use in Context

Directions: Complete each sentence with a word from above.
Read the finished sentences to a partner.

1. I ___like___ my fat cat.

2. Dan has ___my___ tan cap.

3. ___the___ man sat on the mat.

4. Pam can ___play___ tag.

Connected Text

Directions: Read the poem. Then answer the questions.

My Cat

My cat is big. My cat is fat.
She likes to play with my dad's hat.

My cat is tan. My cat is black.
She likes to play in my backpack.

My cat sees me and finds my lap.
She sits on me and has a nap.

Interact with the Text

Directions: Mark the text.

1. Circle all the words with short a

2. Draw a box around the words that rhyme with cat.

Directions: Write about the text.

3. What does the cat like to do? Tell a partner. Then write about it.

SHe lik play

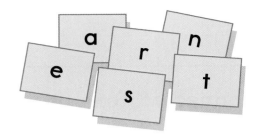

Sort It Out

Directions: Read each word. Then sort the words.
Write each word in the correct box.

bat	can	cat	fan	fat
hat	man	pan	ran	sat

at	an
hat bat cat fat sat	can pan ran man

What did you learn about how words work?

_____

- -

_____

Think and Write

Directions: Listen to each picture name.
Write the spelling for each sound in a separate box.

1.

2.

3.

Listen and Spell

Directions: Write each word and sentence that you hear.

1. _____   2. _____

3. _____   4. _____

5. _____

Make New Words

Directions: Make words with the letter cards on page 440.
Write the words on the lines.

Name _____

What Do We Like?

I am Sam.

I can play soccer.

I like my dog, Rags.

Rags likes to play, too.

1

Fold

I am Dad.

I like my hats.

Big hats. Little hats.

Do you like my hats?

4

2

I am Pam.
I like to play the piano.
What can you play?

Fold

Fold

I am Max.
Dan is my friend.
He has a bat.
What do we like to play?

3

Build Fluency

Directions: Complete each sentence. Use at least one word
with short i.

1. This is _____.

2. We like _____.

3. I play _____.

4. What did _____?

Directions: Write a sentence using each word pair.

5. | lid, pan | _____

6. | big, nap | _____

Word Ladder

Directions: Listen to each clue. Then write the word.
Start at the bottom and climb to the top.

It is on the top of a jar.
Change one letter.

The cat that was scared
by the noise did this.
Change one letter.

This word is the opposite
of "hers."
Change one letter.

What a person at bat
wants to do.
Change one letter.

You need a chair to
do this.
Change one letter.

Start ➞

b i t

Write About It

Directions: Read "What Is It?" again.
Write what you learned about animals.

Fluency Check

Directions: Listen to the child read the word list. Mark one check in the green box if the word is read correctly (accuracy). Mark another check in the blue box if it is read automatically (fluency).

Lesson	Word		
CUMULATIVE ASSESSMENT			
2	bit	☐	☐
	lick	☐	☐
	him	☐	☐
	kits	☐	☐
1	at	☐	☐
	map	☐	☐
	had	☐	☐
	rags	☐	☐

Number Correct (accuracy): _____ / 8

Number Automatic (fluency): _____ / 8

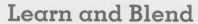

Learn and Blend

Directions: Listen and join in.

o…o…o…
Turn the light on.
o…o…o…
Turn the light off.

Short o

o

Blend It

Directions: Chorally read the words.

INTRODUCE

1. mop	top	hop	hot	not	got
2. dot	dog	lot	log	pot	pop
3. fox	fix	hot	hat	map	mop
4. on	sock	box	jog	rock	logs

5. The frog can hop.

6. It can hop on top of the rock.

REVIEW

7. bag	lip	sad	did	fit	has
8. man	pig	tip	van	zip	can

CHALLENGE

9. mop	mops	dog	dogs	lock	locks

Daily Practice

Directions: Do one activity each day. Then check the box.

☐ Build Fluency Read the words each day by yourself and to a partner.

☐ Mark It Circle all the words with short o.

☐ Spell It Have a partner say each word. Write the word. Check your answer.

☐ Write About It Use the words to create a story. Draw a box around the words from the list that you used.

Read-Spell-Write

Directions: Write each word two times. Say each letter as you write it.

1. and _____

2. stop _____

3. see _____

4. jump _____

Use in Context

Directions: Complete each sentence with a word from above. Read the finished sentences to a partner.

1. The pot _____ pan are in the box.

2. His dog likes to _____.

3. I _____ to sit on the log.

4. We did not _____ the big fox.

Connected Text

Directions: Read the story. Then answer the questions.

Bob's Job

Bob has a job.
His job is to chop logs.
But Bob has to stop.
It is too hot!
Bob will hop in the pond.
Plop!
Now he is not hot.

Interact with the Text

Directions: Mark the text.

1. Circle all the words with short o.

2. Draw a box around the words that rhyme with chop.

Directions: Write about the text.

3. What is Bob's job? Tell a partner. Then write about it.

Sort It Out

Directions: Read each word. Then sort the words.
Write each word in the correct box.

| dot | got | hop | hot | lot |
| mop | not | pop | pot | top |

op	ot

What did you learn about how words work?

_____

- -

_____

Think and Write

Directions: Listen to each picture name.
Write the spelling for each sound in a separate box.

1.

2.

3.

Listen and Spell

Directions: Write each word and sentence that you hear.

1. _____   2. _____

3. _____   4. _____

5. _____

Make New Words

Directions: Make words with the letter cards on page 440.
Write the words on the lines.

_____

_ _ _ _ _ _ _ _ _ _ _ _ _ _ _ _ _

_____

_ _ _ _ _ _ _ _ _ _ _ _ _ _ _ _ _

_____

_ _ _ _ _ _ _ _ _ _ _ _ _ _ _ _ _

_____

_ _ _ _ _ _ _ _ _ _ _ _ _ _ _ _ _

_____

_ _ _ _ _ _ _ _ _ _ _ _ _ _ _ _ _

_____

_ _ _ _ _ _ _ _ _ _ _ _ _ _ _ _ _

_____

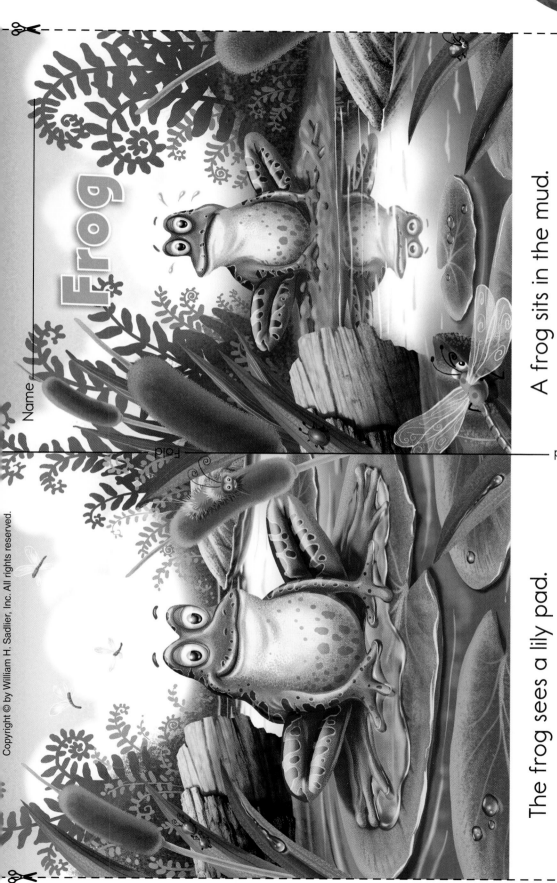

Name

Frog

I

A frog sits in the mud.

The mud gets hot.

Hop. Hop. Plop!

The frog jumps in the pond.

Fold

The frog sees a lily pad.

The frog sits on the lily pad.

The lily pad is not hot. STOP!

The frog sits and sits on the
cool lily pad.

4

2

The frog sees a rock.

The frog sits on the rock.

The rock gets hot.

Hop. Hop. Plop!

The frog jumps in the pond.

3

The frog sees a log.

The frog sits on the log.

The log gets hot.

Hop. Hop. Plop!

The frog jumps in the pond.

Fold

Fold

Double Final Consonants (ll, ss, zz)

Directions: Write a double final consonant from the box to make a word.
Then write the word.

| ll | ss | zz |

1.  hi____

2. pa____

3.  mi____

4.  fi____

5. 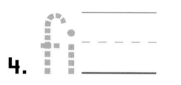 do____

6.  ja____

Directions: Write a sentence using a word you wrote.

7. _____

Read and Write

Directions: Say each picture name. Circle the word for the picture.
Write it on the line.

1.
map
mop
top
_____

2.
dig
dog
jog
_____

3.
box
rock
sock
_____

4.
hip
hop
top
_____

5.
box
fox
ox
_____

6.
pat
pop
pot
_____

Build Fluency

Directions: Complete each sentence. Use at least one word with **short o**.

1. They like _____.

2. I jump _____.

3. We see _____.

4. What do _____?

Directions: Write a sentence using each word pair.

5. | not, wig | _____ |

6. | log, sat | _____ |

Word Ladder

Directions: Listen to each clue. Then write the word.
Start at the bottom and climb to the top.

You see this on top
of the letter "i."
Change one letter.

_____ _____ _____

A flower can be
planted in this.
Change one letter.

_____ _____ _____

You might feel this on
a sunny summer day.
Change one letter.

_____ _____ _____

You can do this on
one foot.
Change one letter.

_____ _____ _____

This is a toy you
can spin.
Change one letter.

_____ _____ _____

Start ➡

m o p

Write About It

Directions: Read "Frog" again.
Write what you learned about the frog.

Fluency Check

Directions: Listen to the child read the word list. Mark one check in the green box if the word is read correctly (accuracy). Mark another check in the blue box if it is read automatically (fluency).

CUMULATIVE ASSESSMENT			
Lesson	Word		
3	mop	☐	☐
	box	☐	☐
	dot	☐	☐
	log	☐	☐
2	bit	☐	☐
	lick	☐	☐
	him	☐	☐
	kits	☐	☐
I	at	☐	☐
	map	☐	☐
	had	☐	☐
	rags	☐	☐
Number Correct (accuracy): _____ / 12			
Number Automatic (fluency): _____ / 12			

Learn and Blend

Directions: Listen and join in.

u…u…u…
Up goes the umbrella.

Short u

u

Blend It

Directions: Chorally read the words.

INTRODUCE

1. up	cup	pup	but	cut	hut
2. cup	cut	bug	bun	hug	hum
3. cap	cup	pop	pup	bug	bag
4. bus	dug	fun	gum	jug	nut

5. The big red bug hid.

6. The big red bug hid under the rug.

REVIEW

7. map	led	hip	rock	dot	rip
8. fell	tap	fog	beg	tan	lid

CHALLENGE

9. truck	stuck	struck	fluff	stuff	plug

Daily Practice

Directions: Do one activity each day. Then check the box.

☐ **Build Fluency** Read the words each day by yourself and to a partner.

☐ **Mark It** Circle all the words with short u.

☐ **Spell It** Have a partner say each word. Write the word. Check your answer.

☐ **Write About It** Use the words to create a story. Draw a box around the words from the list that you used.

Read-Spell-Write

Directions: Write each word two times. Say each letter as you write it.

1. little _____

2. with _____

3. have _____

4. are _____

Use in Context

Directions: Complete each sentence with a word from above. Read the finished sentences to a partner.

1. I hug my _____ pup.

2. We _____ fun on the bus.

3. What did I do _____ the six cups?

4. My cap and bat _____ in the mud.

Connected Text

Directions: **Read the story. Then answer the questions.**

Fun in the Sun

We can have fun in the sun.
Lots of fun!
We can run up to the sea
and jump in.
But too much sun is not good
for our skin.
So after a swim we get our hats
and sit under a big umbrella.

Interact with the Text

Directions: **Mark the text.**

1. Circle all the words with short u.

2. Draw a box around the words that rhyme with sun.

Directions: **Write about the text.**

3. How can we have fun in the sun? Tell a partner. Then write about it.

Word Sort

Sort It Out

Directions: Read each word. Then sort the words.
Write each word in the correct box.

bug	bun	cut	dug	fun
hug	nut	rug	run	sun

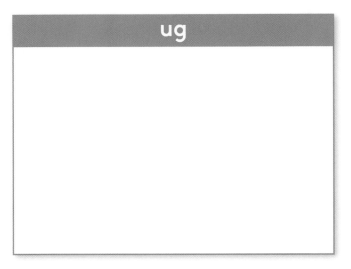

un

ug

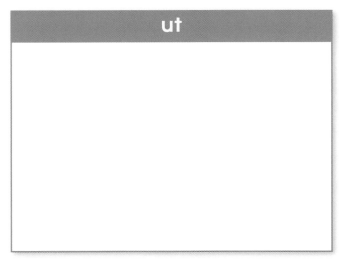

ut

What did you learn about how words work?

Think and Write

Directions: Listen to each picture name.
Write the spelling for each sound in a separate box.

1.

2.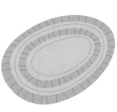

3.

Listen and Spell

Directions: Write each word and sentence that you hear.

1. _____   2. _____

3. _____   4. _____

5. _____

Make New Words

Directions: Make words with the letter cards on page 440.
Write the words on the lines.

—1—

Name _____

Little Bugs, Big Bugs

Fold

Bugs are little.
Bugs are big.
Bugs sit on a leaf.
Bugs crawl on a twig.

Fold

Bugs can fly.
Bugs have wings.
Bugs can buzz.
Bugs can sting.

4

2

Bugs are black.
Bugs are red.
Bugs have six legs.
Bugs have little heads.

Bugs with stripes.
Bugs with spots.
Bugs with a few.
Bugs with lots.

3

Fold

Fold

Double Final Consonants (**dd, ll, zz**)

Directions: Write a double final consonant from the box to make a word.
Then write the word.

dd	ll	zz

1.  wi____ _____

2.  a____ _____

3.  bu____ _____

4. o____ _____

5.  pu____ _____

6.  pi____ _____

Directions: Write a sentence using a word you wrote.

7. _____

Read and Write

Directions: Say each picture name. Circle the word for the picture.
Write it on the line.

cap

cup

cut

1. _____

hat

hit

hut

2. _____

bag

big

bug

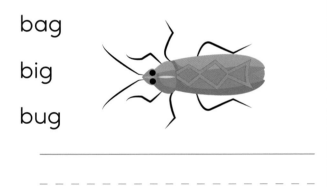

3. _____

fun

ran

run

4. _____

tab

top

tub

5. _____

rag

rug

tug

6. _____

Build Fluency

Directions: Complete each sentence. Use at least one word with short u.

1. This is _____.

2. I have _____.

3. The little _____.

4. Jim and I _____.

Directions: Write a sentence using each word pair.

5. | bus, hot | _____

6. | cup, mat | _____

Word Ladder

Directions: Listen to each clue. Then write the word.
Start at the bottom and climb to the top.

What you have when
you play with friends.

Change one letter.

_____ _____ _____

It shines during the day
to give us light.

Change one letter.

_____ _____ _____

Use this for your
sandwich.

Change one letter.

_____ _____ _____

You might find one
crawling in the dirt.

Change one letter.

_____ _____ _____

What the dog did to get
the bone he buried.

Change one letter.

_____ _____ _____

Start ➡ r u g

Write About It

Directions: Read "Little Bugs, Big Bugs" again.
Write what you learned about bugs.

Fluency Check

Directions: **Listen to the child read the word list. Mark one check in the green box if the word is read correctly (accuracy). Mark another check in the blue box if it is read automatically (fluency).**

CUMULATIVE ASSESSMENT

Lesson	Word			Lesson	Word		
4	hug	☐	☐	2	bit	☐	☐
	buns	☐	☐		lick	☐	☐
	fuzz	☐	☐		him	☐	☐
	nut	☐	☐		kits	☐	☐
3	mop	☐	☐	1	at	☐	☐
	box	☐	☐		map	☐	☐
	dot	☐	☐		had	☐	☐
	log	☐	☐		rags	☐	☐

Number Correct (accuracy): _____ / 16

Number Automatic (fluency): _____ / 16

Learn and Blend

Directions: Listen and join in.

e…e…e…
Slowly goes the engine
up the hill.

Short e
e

Blend It

Directions: Chorally read the words.

INTRODUCE

1. set	let	get	red	bed	led
2. met	men	yet	yes	beg	bet
3. pen	pan	pin	bad	bed	bid
4. pet	bell	egg	vet	leg	mess

5. Let's get a red pen.

6. Is the egg in the nest?

REVIEW

7. cup	box	sat	big	fan	lips
8. got	run	bugs	dig	zap	mix

CHALLENGE

9. let   letting   get   getting   pet   petting

Daily Practice

Directions: Do one activity each day. Then check the box.

☐ Build Fluency Read the words each day by yourself and to a partner.
☐ Mark It Circle all the words with short e.
☐ Spell It Have a partner say each word. Write the word. Check your answer.
☐ Write About It Use the words to create a story. Draw a box around the words from the list that you used.

Read-Spell-Write
Directions: Write each word two times. Say each letter as you write it.

1. give _____

2. come _____

3. some _____

4. for _____

Use in Context
Directions: Complete each sentence with a word from above.
Read the finished sentences to a partner.

1. The red pen is _____ him.

2. I will get _____ eggs.

3. _____ play with Ned and Ted.

4. Do not _____ up yet!

Connected Text

Directions: **Read the letter. Then answer the questions.**

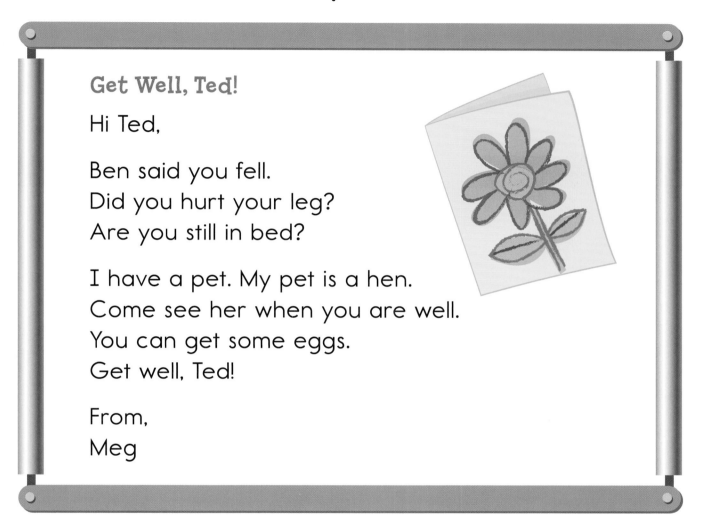

Get Well, Ted!

Hi Ted,

Ben said you fell.
Did you hurt your leg?
Are you still in bed?

I have a pet. My pet is a hen.
Come see her when you are well.
You can get some eggs.
Get well, Ted!

From,
Meg

Interact with the Text

Directions: **Mark the text.**

1. Circle all the words with short e.

2. Draw a box around the words that rhyme with pet.

Directions: **Write about the text.**

3. What pet does Meg have? Tell a partner. Then write about it.

Word Sort

Sort It Out

Directions: Read each word. Then sort the words.
Write each word in the correct box.

bell	get	let	men	net
pen	sell	tell	ten	wet

ell

et

en

What did you learn about how words work?

_____

- -

_____

Think and Write

Directions: Listen to each picture name. Write the spelling for each sound in a separate box.

1.

2.

3.

Listen and Spell

Directions: Write each word and sentence that you hear.

1. _____

2. _____

3. _____

4. _____

5. _____

Make New Words

Directions: Make words with the letter cards on page 440.
Write the words on the lines.

_____

- - - - - - - - - - - - - - - - -

_____

_____

- - - - - - - - - - - - - - - - -

_____

_____

- - - - - - - - - - - - - - - - -

_____

_____

- - - - - - - - - - - - - - - - -

_____

_____

- - - - - - - - - - - - - - - - -

_____

_____

- - - - - - - - - - - - - - - - -

_____

1

Name _____

Birds and Their Nests

Birds make nests.

Big nests.

Little nests.

Nests filled with eggs.

All kinds of nests!

Fold

This nest is in mud.

It was dug like a pit.

The nest gives a duck a wet place to sit!

4

2

This nest is in a tree.
It is made of some sticks.
It is a nest for a wren.
It is a bed for her chicks.

This nest is a hole
in a cactus out west.
It is home to an elf owl
who comes there to rest.

3

Fold

Plurals

Directions: Add s to each word to make a word that means more than one.
Then write the word.

1.  pup ___ _____

2.  bat ___ _____

3.  log ___ _____

4.  bell ___ _____

5.  wig ___ _____

6.  egg ___ _____

Directions: Write a sentence using a word that shows more than one from above.

7. _____

Read and Write

Directions: Say each picture name. Circle the word for the picture. Write it on the line.

bed red rid	bag beg bug
1. _____	**2.** _____
jam jet jug	leg let log
3. _____	**4.** _____
met net not	pen tan ten 10
5. _____	**6.** _____

Build Fluency

Directions: Complete each sentence. Use at least one word with **short e**.

1. My house _____ .

2. Give me _____ .

3. Come see _____ .

4. There are _____ .

Directions: Write a sentence using each word pair.

5. | mop, wet |

6. | can, get |

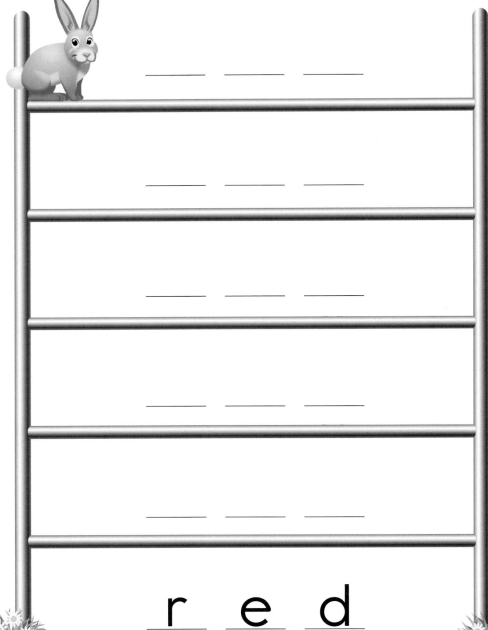

Word Ladder

Directions: Listen to each clue. Then write the word.
Start at the bottom and climb to the top.

This word means "to allow."

Change one letter.

This word is the past tense of "lead."

Change one letter.

It is part of your body.

Change one letter.

What a dog might do to get a treat.

Change one letter.

You sleep in this at night.

Change one letter.

Start ➔

r e d

Write About It

Directions: Read "Birds and Their Nests" again.
Write what you learned about birds.

Fluency Check

Directions: Listen to the child read the word list. Mark one check in the green box if the word is read correctly (accuracy). Mark another check in the blue box if it is read automatically (fluency).

CUMULATIVE ASSESSMENT							
Lesson	**Word**			**Lesson**	**Word**		
5	egg	☐	☐	**2**	bit	☐	☐
	pens	☐	☐		lick	☐	☐
	beg	☐	☐		him	☐	☐
	let	☐	☐		kits	☐	☐
4	hug	☐	☐	**1**	at	☐	☐
	buns	☐	☐		map	☐	☐
	fuzz	☐	☐		had	☐	☐
	nut	☐	☐		rags	☐	☐
3	mop	☐	☐				
	box	☐	☐				
	dot	☐	☐				
	log	☐	☐				

Number Correct (accuracy): _____ / 20

Number Automatic (fluency): _____ / 20

UNIT 2

Dear Family,

In this unit, your child will learn about words that contain short vowels with blends and digraphs. He or she will learn to read words with l-blends, s-blends, and r-blends such as **flag**; **smell**; and **trip**. Your child will also learn to read words with the digraphs **sh**, **th**, **ch**, **tch**, **wh**, **ng**, and **nk**, such as **shop**; **that**; **chat**; **match**; **when**; **king**; and **sink**.

Read Connected Text

For each week's lesson, your child will read a Take-Home Book that focuses on the lesson skills. At week's end, the book will be sent home with your child. Read the book to your child, or read it aloud together, pointing to each word as you say it. Multiple readings will give your child practice with the lesson skills.

Practice with the Take-Home Book

Ask your child to point to words in the story that include short vowels with blends or digraphs.

Have your child tell you about the book in one sentence. Write what your child says and read the description aloud together.

Lesson Skills and Take-Home Books

Lesson 6 l-Blends: "What Are These Things?"
Lesson 7 s-Blends: "The Best Snack"
Lesson 8 r-Blends: "Brad and Trent"
Lesson 9 Digraphs **sh**, **th**: "The Big Wish"
Lesson 10 Digraphs **ch**, **tch**, **wh**: "Will We Win?"
Lesson 11 Digraphs **ng**, **nk**: "The King's Song"

Extend the Learning

With your child, look for words with short vowels with blends and digraphs in books, signs, magazine covers, etc. Keep a notebook of words you discover. Challenge your child to identify objects in your home or other locations that have short vowels with blends and digraphs. For example, "I spy a ring."

 Visit SadlierConnect.com for **Student & Family Resources.**

Apreciada familia:

Conexión con el Hogar

En esta unidad, su niño(a) aprenderá acerca de palabras con vocales con sonidos cortos y consonantes combinadas, y dígrafos. Aprenderá a leer palabras con combinaciones de la l, de la s, y de la r, como **flag**; **smell** y **trip**. Su niño(a) aprenderá también a leer palabras con los dígrafos **sh**, **th**, **ch**, **tch**, **wh**, **ng** y **nk**, como **shop**; **that**; **chat**; **match**; **when**; **king** y **sink**.

Leyendo la historieta en el Take-Home Book

Para cada lección de la semana su niño(a) leerá un cuadernillo de historietas, Take-Home Book, que se enfoca en las destrezas de la lección. Al final de cada semana su niño(a) llevará el cuadernillo a la casa. Lea la historieta a su niño(a) o léanla en voz alta juntos, señalando cada palabra al decirla. Leer varias veces ayudará a su niño(a) a practicar las destrezas de la lección.

Practicando con el Take-Home Book

Pida a su niño(a) señalar palabras en la historieta con vocales con sonido corto y consonantes combinadas, y dígrafos para esa lección. Luego pídale que resuma la historieta en una frase. Escriba lo que dice su niño(a) y lean juntos lo que escribió.

Lesson Skills and Take-Home Books
Lesson 6 l-Blends: "What Are These Things?"
Lesson 7 s-Blends: "The Best Snack"
Lesson 8 r-Blends: "Brand and Trent"
Lesson 9 Digraghs **sh**, **th**: "The Big Wish"
Lesson 10 Digraghs **ch**, **tch**, **wh**: "Will We Win?"
Lesson 11 Digraghs **ng**, **nk**: "The King's Song"

Ampliando el aprendizaje

Con su niño(a) busque palabras con vocales con sonidos cortos y consonantes combinadas, y dígrafos en libros, letreros, portadas de revistas, etc. Haga una libreta con palabras que descubran juntos. Rete a su niño(a) a identificar, ya sea en su casa o en otros lugares, objetos con vocales con sonidos cortos y consonantes combinadas, y dígrafos. Por ejemplo: "I spy a ring."

 Visite SadlierConnect.com para recursos para el estudiante y la familia.

Learn and Blend

Directions: Listen and join in.

fl…fl…fl…
Flip, flop, flip.
When it's wet you might slip.

l-Blends

bl	cl	fl
gl	pl	sl

Blend It

Directions: Chorally read the words.

INTRODUCE

1. lip | slip | back | black | lock | block
2. cap | clap | cub | club | pan | plan
3. flip | flop | flap | flag | flat | fat
4. clap | clam | slam | slap | sled | glad
5. The bug is red and black.
6. Can you see the little flag?

REVIEW

7. yes | men | bug | us | mom | hop
8. fix | sits | bags | bad | mess | buzz

CHALLENGE

9. slipping | clapping | stopping | skipping | flipping | sledding

Daily Practice

Directions: Do one activity each day. Then check the box.

☐ Build Fluency Read the words each day by yourself and to a partner.
☐ Mark It Circle all the words with bl. Underline all the words with fl.
☐ Spell It Have a partner say each word. Write the word. Check your answer.
☐ Write About It Use the words to create a story. Draw a box around the words from the list that you used.

Read-Spell-Write
Directions: Write each word two times. Say each letter as you write it.

1. many _____

2. thing _____

3. you _____

4. these _____

Use in Context
Directions: Complete each sentence with a word from above.
Read the finished sentences to a partner.

1. I like to play with _____ blocks.

2. _____ bugs are on the flat rock.

3. The black _____ is a bug.

4. Clap if _____ like what you see!

Connected Text

Directions: **Read the plan. Then answer the questions.**

The Plan for the Play

Get set!
The class will put on a play.
There are many things to do.
This is the plan.
We can write the words.
We can make a big blue sky.
We can put flags up and down the block.
We can tell friends to come!

Interact with the Text

Directions: **Mark the text.**

1. Circle all the words with l-blend spellings.

2. Draw a box around the words that rhyme with can.

Directions: **Write about the text.**

3. What does the class plan to put on? Tell a partner. Then write about it.

Sort It Out

Directions: Read each word. Then sort the words.
Write each word in the correct box.

| black | block | clap | class | clock |
| club | flag | flat | flip | flop |

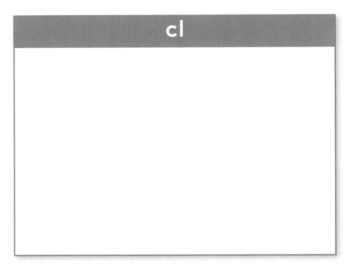

bl

cl

fl

What did you learn about how words work?

Think and Write

Directions: Listen to each picture name. Write the spelling for each sound in a separate box.

1.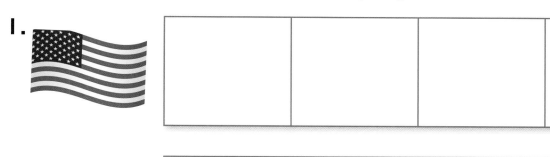

2.

3.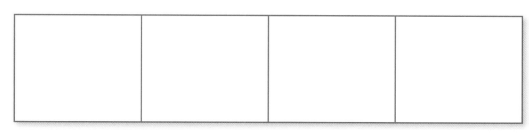

Listen and Spell

Directions: Write each word and sentence that you hear.

1. _____

2. _____

3. _____

4. _____

5. _____

Make New Words

Directions: Make words with the letter cards on page 440.
Write the words on the lines.

Possessives

Directions: Circle the word that completes each sentence.
Write the word on the line.

dogs, dog's

1. The _____ paw is big.

kids, kid's

2. The _____ like to play.

cats, cat's

3. My _____ can run.

moms, mom's

4. My _____ job is fun.

bugs, bug's

5. The _____ spots are black.

dads, dad's

6. My _____ cap is red.

Directions: Write a sentence using one of the words you wrote.

7. _____

Read and Write

Directions: Say each picture name. Circle the word for the picture.
Write it on the line.

back
black
block

1. _____

plug
plum
plus

2. _____

clap
cliff
clip

3. _____

slap
sled
slid

4. _____

plan
plop
plug

5. _____

clam
clap
clip

6. _____

Build Fluency

Directions: Complete each sentence. Use at least one word with an l-blend.

1. We see _____.

2. You have _____.

3. These are _____.

4. I stop _____.

Directions: Write a sentence using each word pair.

his, plan

5. _____

club, met

6. _____

Word Ladder

Directions: Listen to each clue. Then write the word.
Start at the bottom and climb to the top.

The outside part of your mouth
Change one letter.

_____ _____ _____

People use this to hold papers together.
Change one letter.

_____ _____ _____ _____

People do this at the end of a good show.
Change one letter.

_____ _____ _____ _____

To hit
Change one letter.

_____ _____ _____ _____

To slide on an icy sidewalk
Change one letter.

_____ _____ _____ _____

Start → f l i p

Write About It

Directions: Read "What Are These Things?" again.
Write what you learned about in the story.

Fluency Check

Directions: Listen to the child read the word list. Mark one check in the green box if the word is read correctly (accuracy). Mark another check in the blue box if it is read automatically (fluency).

CUMULATIVE ASSESSMENT							
Lesson	**Word**			**Lesson**	**Word**		
6	clip	☐	☐	**3**	mop	☐	☐
	flap	☐	☐		box	☐	☐
	block	☐	☐		dot	☐	☐
	glad	☐	☐		log	☐	☐
5	egg	☐	☐	**2**	bit	☐	☐
	pens	☐	☐		lick	☐	☐
	beg	☐	☐		him	☐	☐
	let	☐	☐		kits	☐	☐
4	hug	☐	☐	**1**	at	☐	☐
	buns	☐	☐		map	☐	☐
	fuzz	☐	☐		had	☐	☐
	nut	☐	☐		rags	☐	☐

Number Correct (accuracy): _____ / 24

Number Automatic (fluency): _____ / 24

Learn and Blend

Directions: Listen and join in.

sm…sm…sm…
Smell the sweet flowers.
Achoo!

s-Blends			
sc	sk	sl	sm
sn	sp	st	sw

Blend It

Directions: Chorally read the words.

INTRODUCE

1. lip	slip	kid	skid	pin	spin
2. sack	snack	sell	smell	pot	spot
3. spill	spell	spot	stop	step	stem
4. sled	swim	skit	spend	skin	snap

5. I smell a skunk.

6. Do not spill Bob's milk!

REVIEW

7. black	flag	get	red	legs	hug
8. bus	socks	jog	quit	digs	pass

CHALLENGE

9. spelling spelled smelling smelled smashing smashed

Daily Practice

Directions: Do one activity each day. Then check the box.

☐ **Build Fluency** Read the words each day by yourself and to a partner.

☐ **Mark It** Circle all the words with **sp**. Underline all the words with **st**.

☐ **Spell It** Have a partner say each word. Write the word. Check your answer.

☐ **Write About It** Use the words to create a story. Draw a box around the words from the list that you used.

Read-Spell-Write

Directions: Write each word two times. Say each letter as you write it.

1. call _____

2. from _____

3. which _____

4. very _____

Use in Context

Directions: Complete each sentence with a word from above.
Read the finished sentences to a partner.

1. Ask Pam to _____ him back.

2. _____ sled is his?

3. The dog runs _____ fast.

4. I got the snack _____ Bob.

Connected Text

Directions: **Read the directions. Then answer the questions.**

Skip, Stomp, and Spin

Ask your friends to play this game.
It is the best! Say:

- I will call your name.

- Line up and stand still.

- I will yell, "Go!"

- Skip to that stick.

- Stomp your feet. Do not stop!

- Spin very fast.

- Take a step and stop.

- Smile and get some rest!

Interact with the Text

Directions: **Mark the text.**

1. Circle all the words with s-blend spellings.

2. Draw a box around the word that rhymes with best.

Directions: **Write about the text.**

3. How do you spin? Tell a partner. Then write about it.

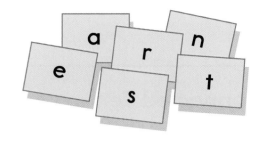

Sort It Out

Directions: Read each word. Then sort the words.
Write each word in the correct box.

slap	sled	slip	snap	sniff
snug	stem	stick	stop	stuff

sl

sn

st

What did you learn about how words work?

_____

- -

_____

Think and Write

Directions: Listen to each picture name.
Write the spelling for each sound in a separate box.

1.

2.

3.

Listen and Spell

Directions: Write each word and sentence that you hear.

1. _____

2. _____

3. _____

4. _____

5. _____

Make New Words

Directions: Make words with the letter cards on page 442.
Write the words on the lines.

_____
- - - - - - - - - - - - - - - - -
_____

_____
- - - - - - - - - - - - - - - - -
_____

_____
- - - - - - - - - - - - - - - - -
_____

_____
- - - - - - - - - - - - - - - - -
_____

_____
- - - - - - - - - - - - - - - - -
_____

_____
- - - - - - - - - - - - - - - - -
_____

The Best Snack

Name _____

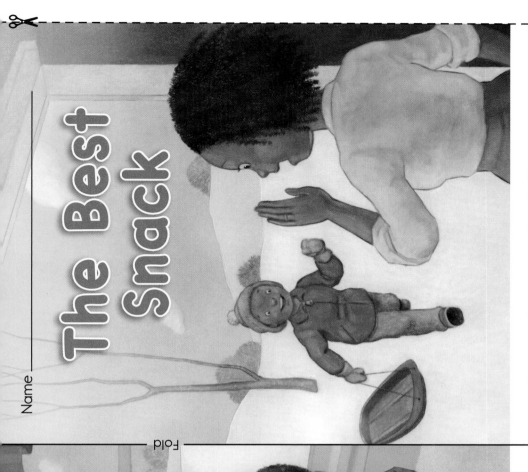

1

Scott sleds on the hill.

Up and down. Up and down.

Mom calls from home.

Stop! Time for a snack.

Fold

Fold

"This snack is the best!" says Scott.

"But I am still hungry."

"Go play," says Mom.

4

2

He sees lots of snacks.

He sniffs. The smell . . . yum!

"Which snack is for me?" asks
Scott.

Fold

Mom gives Scott a snack.

Scott gets a glass of milk.

"Do not spill it," says Mom.

3

Final Blends

Directions: Say the name of the picture. Circle the blend that ends the picture name. Write the picture name on the line.

1.
lp
nt
mp

te_____

2.
mp
lt
st

be_____

3.
nd
lp
mp

la_____

4.
nd
ft
lt

gi_____

5.
nd
ld
sk

po_____

6.
sk
st
nd

ma_____

Read and Write

Directions: Say each picture name. Circle the word for the picture.
Write it on the line.

stem

swim

swing

1. _____

slam

sled

slip

2. _____

slap

smell

spill

3. _____

spill

spin

spot

4. _____

spin

spot

swing

5. _____

stem

step

stop

6. _____

Build Fluency

Directions: **Complete each sentence. Use at least one word with an s-blend.**

1. We see _____.

2. I have some _____.

3. Do you _____?

4. These are very _____.

Directions: **Write a sentence using each word pair.**

5. flag, spill

_____

6. clap, stop

_____

Word Ladder

Directions: Listen to each clue. Then write the word.
Start at the bottom and climb to the top.

A small branch that
fell from a tree
Change two letters.

_____ _____ _____ _____ _____

This word describes you
when you sit quietly.
Change one letter.

_____ _____ _____ _____ _____

Oops! This happens
when you tip over
your drink.
Take away one letter.
Add two letters.

_____ _____ _____ _____ _____

To turn quickly
Change one letter.

_____ _____ _____ _____

You peel this from
an apple.
Change one letter.

_____ _____ _____ _____

Start → s   k   i   p

Write About It

Directions: Read "The Best Snack" again.
Write what you learned about Scott's favorite snack.

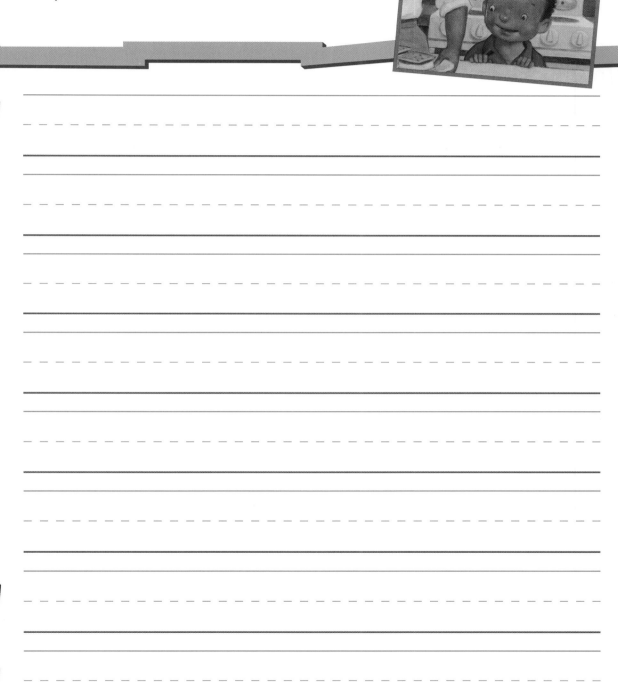

Fluency Check

Directions: Listen to the child read the word list. Mark one check in the green box if the word is read correctly (accuracy). Mark another check in the blue box if it is read automatically (fluency).

CUMULATIVE ASSESSMENT									
Lesson	Word				Lesson	Word			
7	snap	☐	☐		**4**	hug	☐	☐	
	stem	☐	☐			buns	☐	☐	
	spend	☐	☐			fuzz	☐	☐	
	skin	☐	☐			nut	☐	☐	
6	clip	☐	☐		**3**	mop	☐	☐	
	flap	☐	☐			box	☐	☐	
	block	☐	☐			dot	☐	☐	
	glad	☐	☐			log	☐	☐	
5	egg	☐	☐		**2**	bit	☐	☐	
	pens	☐	☐			lick	☐	☐	
	beg	☐	☐			him	☐	☐	
	let	☐	☐			kits	☐	☐	

Number Correct (accuracy): _____ / 24

Number Automatic (fluency): _____ / 24

Learn and Blend

Directions: Listen and join in.

dr…dr…dr…
Drip drop. Drip drop.
The rain falls quietly
on top.

r-Blends			
br	cr	dr	fr
gr		pr	tr

Blend It

Directions: Chorally read the words.

INTRODUCE

1.	tap	trap	tick	trick	fog	frog
2.	cab	crab	grab	rip	grip	trip
3.	drip	drop	track	truck	trick	trim
4.	press	brick	crack	crib	grin	grass

5. Fran has a pet crab.

6. Max is on a big trip.

REVIEW

7.	spell	stop	flat	block	eggs	bell
8.	fun	sun	mix	box	did	win

CHALLENGE

9. trapping   tricking   grabbing ripping   dripping   dropping

Daily Practice

Directions: Do one activity each day. Then check the box.

☐ **Build Fluency** Read the words each day by yourself and to a partner.

☐ **Mark It** Circle all the words with **gr**. Underline all the words with **tr**.

☐ **Spell It** Have a partner say each word. Write the word. Check your answer.

☐ **Write About It** Use the words to create a story. Draw a box around words from the list that you used.

Read-Spell-Write

Directions: Write each word two times. Say each letter as you write it.

1. said _____

2. when _____

3. there _____

4. where _____

Use in Context

Directions: Complete each sentence with a word from above. Read the finished sentences to a partner.

1. _____ can you fix the clock?

2. "I have a red dress," _____ Jill.

3. _____ can we get some crabs?

4. _____ is the little frog.

Connected Text

Directions: **Read the clues. Then answer the questions.**

What Is It?

1. It is where my brother naps.
Mom puts him in it.
When Mom takes him out of it, he grins.
What is it?   (Answer: crib)

2. There is a nest in it.
It has a black trunk. The rest of it is green.
What is it?   (Answer: tree)

3. You can hit it with a stick
or with your hand. When you hit it,
it goes *trum-pum-pum.*
What is it?   (Answer: drum)

Interact with the Text

Directions: **Mark the text.**

1. Circle all the words with r-blend spellings.

2. Draw a box around the word that rhymes with *trum-pum-pum.*

Directions: **Write about the text.**

3. Where does the brother nap? Tell a partner. Then write about it.

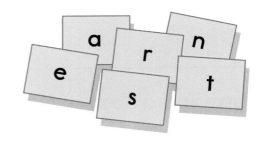

Word Sort

Sort It Out

Directions: Read each word. Then sort the words. Write each word in the correct box.

| crab | crib | dress | drip | drop |
| grab | grass | grin | trap | trick |

cr

dr

gr

tr

What did you learn about how words work?

_____

- -

_____

Think and Write

Directions: Listen to each picture name.
Write the spelling for each sound in a separate box.

1.

2.

3.

Listen and Spell

Directions: Write each word and sentence that you hear.

1. _____

2. _____

3. _____

4. _____

5. _____

Make New Words

Directions: Make words with the letter cards on page 442.
Write the words on the lines.

r-Blends • Lesson 8

Name _____

Brad and Trent

Hi Brad,

I can't wait to see you!

We can play with my trucks.

Your friend, Trent

Fold

Fold

Hi Trent,

I live at 10 Grand Street.

See you at six!

Your friend, Brad

4

2

Hi Trent,

I can't wait to see you, too!

We can play with my drums.

When can you come?

Your friend, Brad

3

Hi Brad,

Mom said I can come at six.

Can we look for frogs, too?

Your friend, Trent

Contractions

Directions: Write the contraction for each pair of words.

1. I am _____

2. she is _____

3. you are _____

4. it is _____

5. they have _____

6. we will _____

Directions: Write a sentence using one of the contractions you wrote.

7. _____

Read and Write

Directions: Say each picture name. Circle the word for the picture.
Write it on the line.

track
trick
truck

1. _____

flag
fog
frog

2. _____

crab
crack
crib

3. _____

drop
drum
trim

4. _____

drill
grill
grip

5. _____

crab
crack
crib

6. _____

Build Fluency

Directions: Complete each sentence. Use at least one word with an r-blend.

1. I see some _____.

2. Many things _____.

3. When is _____?

4. Come with _____.

Directions: Write a sentence using each word pair.

5. grass, slip _____

6. slid, truck _____

Word Ladder

Directions: Listen to each clue. Then write the word.
Start at the bottom and climb to the top.

A way to hold something tightly.

Add one letter.

_____ _____ _____ _____

You can do this to a piece of paper.

Take away one letter.

_____ _____ _____

A tiny bit of water that falls from the faucet.

Change one letter.

_____ _____ _____ _____

When you stumble on a toy you do this.

Change one letter.

_____ _____ _____ _____

A mouse might get caught in one.

Add one letter.

_____ _____ _____ _____

Start ➞   r a p

Write About It

Directions: Read "Brad and Trent" again.
Write what you learned about the two friends.

Fluency Check

Directions: Listen to the child read the word list. Mark one check in the green box if the word is read correctly (accuracy). Mark another check in the blue box if it is read automatically (fluency).

CUMULATIVE ASSESSMENT							
Lesson	**Word**			**Lesson**	**Word**		
8	grass	☐	☐	**5**	egg	☐	☐
	brick	☐	☐		pens	☐	☐
	crop	☐	☐		beg	☐	☐
	can't	☐	☐		let	☐	☐
7	snap	☐	☐	**4**	hug	☐	☐
	stem	☐	☐		buns	☐	☐
	spend	☐	☐		fuzz	☐	☐
	skin	☐	☐		nut	☐	☐
6	clip	☐	☐	**3**	mop	☐	☐
	flap	☐	☐		box	☐	☐
	block	☐	☐		dot	☐	☐
	glad	☐	☐		log	☐	☐
Number Correct (accuracy): _____ / 24							
Number Automatic (fluency): _____ / 24							

Learn and Blend

Directions: Listen and join in.

sh…sh…sh…
Wish, wish,
wish for quiet.

Digraphs

sh   th

Blend It

Directions: Chorally read the words.

INTRODUCE

1. hip	ship	hop	shop	hot	shot
2. fish	wish	dish	rash	crash	trash
3. hat	that	hen	then	his	this
4. mat	math	bat	bath	tin	thin

5. We like to shop a lot!

6. The ship is big.

REVIEW

7. trick	grass	swim	steps	skip	flip
8. get	beds	cups	rock	dog	locks

CHALLENGE

9. fish   fishing   wish   wishing   dish   dishes

Daily Practice

Directions: Do one activity each day. Then check the box.

☐ Build Fluency Read the words each day by yourself and to a partner.

☐ Mark It Circle all the words with sh. Underline all the words with th.

☐ Spell It Have a partner say each word. Write the word. Check your answer.

☐ Write About It Use the words to create a story. Draw a box around the words from the list that you used.

Read-Spell-Write

Directions: Write each word two times. Say each letter as you write it.

1. were _____

2. gave _____

3. go _____

4. first _____

Use in Context

Directions: Complete each sentence with a word from above.
Read the finished sentences to a partner.

1. Ten fish _____ on the dish.

2. We did not see his _____ trick.

3. Did the man _____ on the ship?

4. Sam _____ the dog a bath.

Connected Text

Directions: **Read the story. Then answer the questions.**

This and That

Mom and Josh went to the shop.

Mom gave Josh a list.

He had to get some of this and some of that.

First on the list was fish.

Josh saw fresh fruit on a shelf.

Josh looked at Mom. Fresh fruit was not on the list.

Mom said, "I think we can make a fruit shake at home."

Josh said, "Let's go home!"

Interact with the Text

Directions: **Mark the text.**

1. Circle all the words with sh.

2. Draw a box around the words with th.

Directions: **Write about the text.**

3. What can Josh and Mom make at home? Tell a partner. Then write about it.

Word Sort

Sort It Out

Directions: Read each word. Then sort the words.
Write each word in the correct box.

| fish | path | ship | shop | shut |
| thick | this | trash | wish | with |

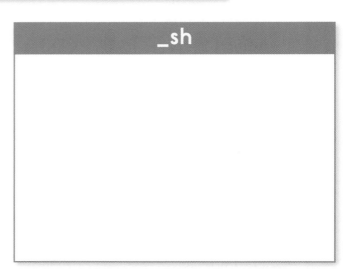

sh_

_sh

th_

_th

What did you learn about how words work?

_____

- -

_____

_____

_____

Think and Write

Directions: Listen to each picture name.
Write the spelling for each sound in a separate box.

1.

2.

3.

Listen and Spell

Directions: Write each word and sentence that you hear.

1. _____   2. _____

3. _____   4. _____

5. _____

Make New Words

Directions: Make words with the letter cards on page 442.
Write the words on the lines.

1

Name _____

The Big Wish

Beth shops with Mom.

First, she sees a dog with spots.

"I wish I had a dog like that!"

"I want that dog for my bath."

Fold

Beth dashed to the bath.

The dog and the fish were in the bath!

How? Mom gave Beth a big smile!

4

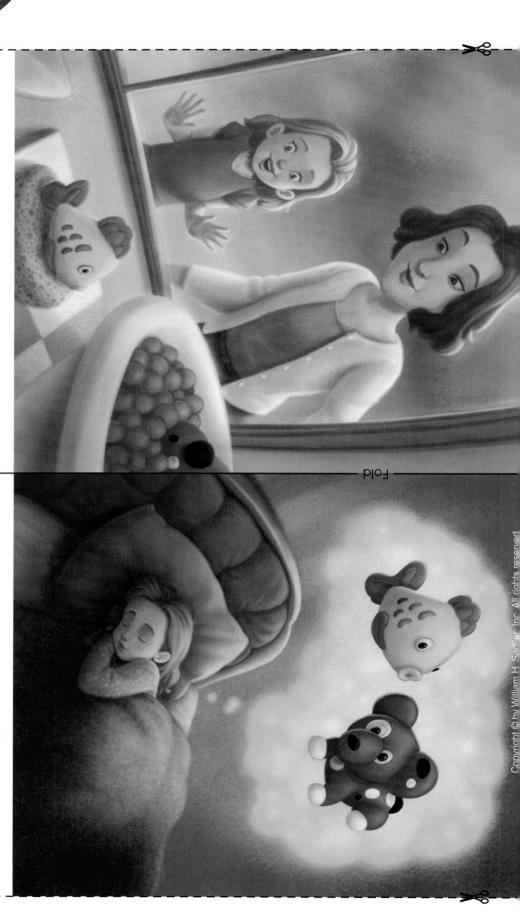

2

Next Beth sees a fish with red fins.

"I wish I had a fish like that!"

"I want that fish for my bath."

"Not now," says Mom.

3

Beth went home sad.

"Go to bed," said Mom.

She gave Beth a big hug.

That night Beth had a dream.

Inflectional Ending **ed**

Directions: Add ed to each word to make a new word.
Then write the new word.

1.  _____

2.  _____

3.  _____

4.  _____

5.  _____

6.  _____

Directions: Complete each sentence with a word you wrote.

7. The sink is _____ with dishes.

8. I _____ the hat to my dad.

Read and Write

Directions: Say each picture name. Circle the word for the picture.
Write it on the line.

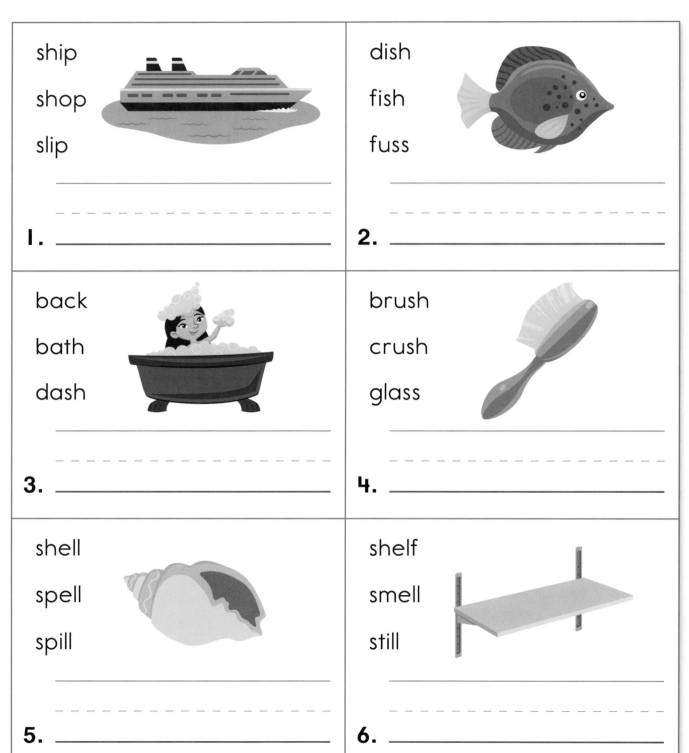

ship

shop

slip

1. _____

dish

fish

fuss

2. _____

back

bath

dash

3. _____

brush

crush

glass

4. _____

shell

spell

spill

5. _____

shelf

smell

still

6. _____

Build Fluency

Directions: Complete each sentence. Use at least one word
with **sh** or **th**.

1. First we _____.

2. There were _____.

3. Where is _____?

4. Can you _____?

Directions: Write a sentence using each word pair.

5. glad, ship _____

6. bath, hot _____

Word Ladder

Directions: Listen to each clue. Then write the word.
Start at the bottom and climb to the top.

Put your food on this.
Take away one letter.
Add two letters.

_____ _____ _____ _____

You can put a carrot in this.
Take away two letters.
Add one letter.

_____ _____ _____

People take trips on the water in this.
Change one letter.

_____ _____ _____ _____ _____

What you do at a store
Add one letter.

_____ _____ _____ _____

How a rabbit will move from place to place
Change one letter.

_____ _____ _____ _____

Start ➜

h i p

Write About It

Directions: Read "The Big Wish" again. Write what you learned about Beth.

Fluency Check

Directions: Listen to the child read the word list. Mark one check in the green box if the word is read correctly (accuracy). Mark another check in the blue box if it is read automatically (fluency).

CUMULATIVE ASSESSMENT

Lesson	Word			Lesson	Word		
9	shop	☐	☐	**6**	clip	☐	☐
	wished	☐	☐		flap	☐	☐
	thin	☐	☐		block	☐	☐
	bath	☐	☐		glad	☐	☐
8	grass	☐	☐	**5**	egg	☐	☐
	brick	☐	☐		pens	☐	☐
	crop	☐	☐		beg	☐	☐
	can't	☐	☐		let	☐	☐
7	snap	☐	☐	**4**	hug	☐	☐
	stem	☐	☐		buns	☐	☐
	spend	☐	☐		fuzz	☐	☐
	skin	☐	☐		nut	☐	☐

Number Correct (accuracy): _____ / 24

Number Automatic (fluency): _____ / 24

Learn and Blend

Directions: Listen and join in.

ch...ch...ch...
Chop the veggies.
wh...wh...wh...
Where is the whale?

Digraphs

ch   tch   wh

Blend It

Directions: Chorally read the words.

INTRODUCE

1. hat	chat	hip	chip	hen	when
2. such	much	lunch	bunch	match	patch
3. cat	catch	mat	match	it	itch
4. when	which	whip	what	bench	inch

5. Chip will catch a big fish.

6. When is lunch?

REVIEW

7. shop	wish	that	math	this	with
8. trick	grass	smell	stop	flash	slip

CHALLENGE

9. lunch	lunchbox	itch	itches	itching	switching

Daily Practice

Directions: Do one activity each day. Then check the box.

☐ Build Fluency Read the words each day by yourself and to a partner.

☐ Mark It Circle all the words with ch. Underline all the words with wh.

☐ Spell It Have a partner say each word. Write the word. Check your answer.

☐ Write About It Use the words to create a story. Draw a box around the words from the list that you used.

Read-Spell-Write

Directions: Write each word two times. Say each letter as you write it.

1. they _____

2. eat _____

3. too _____

4. our _____

Use in Context

Directions: Complete each sentence with a word from above.
Read the finished sentences to a partner.

1. _____ sit on the bench.

2. The hat is much _____ big!

3. Brad sat to _____ his lunch.

4. _____ socks do not match.

Connected Text

Directions: **Read the story. Then answer the questions.**

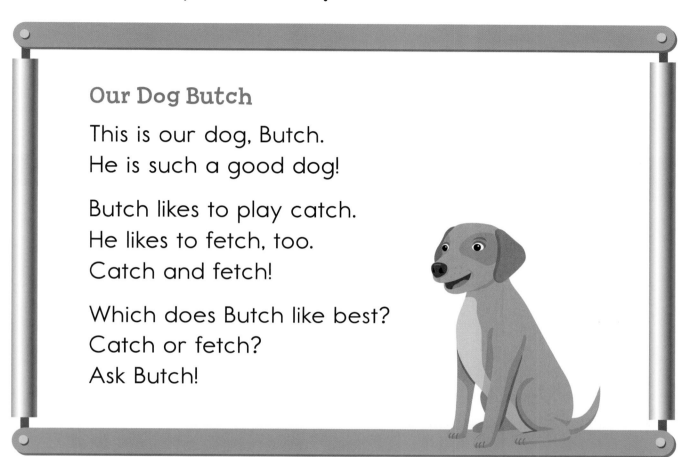

Our Dog Butch

This is our dog, Butch.
He is such a good dog!

Butch likes to play catch.
He likes to fetch, too.
Catch and fetch!

Which does Butch like best?
Catch or fetch?
Ask Butch!

Interact with the Text

Directions: **Mark the text.**

1. Circle all the words with ch.

2. Draw a box around the word with wh.

Directions: **Write about the text.**

3. What does Butch like to do? Tell a partner. Then write about it.

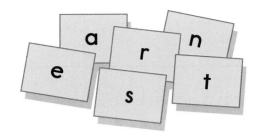

Word Sort

Sort It Out

Directions: Read each word. Then sort the words.
Write each word in the correct box.

| catch | check | chin | chop | itch |
| match | what | when | where | which |

ch_

_tch

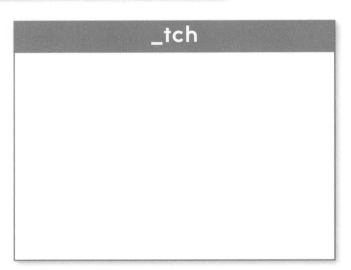

wh_

What did you learn about how words work?

_____

- -

_____

Think and Write

Directions: Listen to each picture name.
Write the spelling for each sound in a separate box.

1.

2.

3.

Listen and Spell

Directions: Write each word and sentence that you hear.

1. _____   2. _____

3. _____   4. _____

5. _____

Make New Words

Directions: Make words with the letter cards on page 442.
Write the words on the lines.

Name _____

Will We Win?

Sandwich Contest

1

"Can we make the best sandwich?" asks Dad.

"Yes," says Mitch.

"Our sandwich will win!"

The judge stops. He sniffs.
Then he gets a big bite.

"This is the best sandwich!" he yells.

"I am eating it all." CHOMP!

4

2

Dad and Mitch cut, cut, cut.
They chop, chop, chop, chop.
They mix, mix, and spread.
Then they stack it up, up, up.

Fold

Which Sandwich Is Best?

They put the sandwich on
a dish. Chips, too.
Then they sit on the bench.
Tick. Tock. Tick. Tock. Will
they win?

3

Inflectional Ending **ing**

Directions: Add ing to each word to make a new word.
Then write the new word.

1. sell _____ _____

2. miss _____ _____

3. add _____ _____

4. fix _____ _____

5. spill _____ _____

6. sketch _____ _____

Directions: Complete each sentence with a word you wrote.

7. A dish is _____ from the box.

8. Is the man _____ plants?

Read and Write

Directions: Say each picture name. Circle the word for the picture.
Write it on the line.

catch
match
math

1. _____

chat
chin
then

2. _____

lunch
much
munch

3. _____

ax
inch
itch

4. _____

check
chest
this

5. _____

batch
bench
fetch

6. _____

Build Fluency

Directions: Complete each sentence. Use at least one word with ch, tch, or wh.

1. I like to eat _____.

2. They will _____.

3. Mom gave _____.

4. Our dog _____.

Directions: Write a sentence using each word pair.

5. patch, where _____

6. chat, with _____

Word Ladder

Directions: Listen to each clue. Then write the word.
Start at the bottom and climb to the top.

When someone throws
you a ball, you do this.
Change one letter.

_____ _____ _____ _____

Two socks that go
together
Change one letter.

_____ _____ _____ _____

To fix or mend
Change one letter.

_____ _____ _____ _____

To throw the ball to the
person at home plate
Add one letter.

_____ _____ _____ _____

It makes you want to
scratch.
Change one letter.

_____ _____ _____ _____

Start ➜

i   n   c   h

Write About It

Directions: Read "Will We Win?" again.
Write what you learned about Mitch.

Fluency Check

Directions: Listen to the child read the word list. Mark one check in the green box if the word is read correctly (accuracy). Mark another check in the blue box if it is read automatically (fluency).

CUMULATIVE ASSESSMENT							
Lesson	Word			Lesson	Word		
10	chip	☐	☐	**7**	snap	☐	☐
	when	☐	☐		stem	☐	☐
	bunch	☐	☐		spend	☐	☐
	matching	☐	☐		skin	☐	☐
9	shop	☐	☐	**6**	clip	☐	☐
	wished	☐	☐		flap	☐	☐
	thin	☐	☐		block	☐	☐
	bath	☐	☐		glad	☐	☐
8	grass	☐	☐	**5**	egg	☐	☐
	brick	☐	☐		pens	☐	☐
	crop	☐	☐		beg	☐	☐
	can't	☐	☐		let	☐	☐

Number Correct (accuracy): _____ / 24

Number Automatic (fluency): _____ / 24

Learn and Blend

Directions: Listen and join in.

ng…ng…ng…
Ding. Dong. The bell
rings and sings.

Digraphs

ng   nk

Blend It

Directions: Chorally read the words.

INTRODUCE

1. ring	king	sing	sting	thing	bring
2. song	long	ink	sink	drink	blink
3. ring	rink	sing	sink	thing	think
4. singing	stinging	thinking	winking	bringing	drinking

5. What did you think?

6. We like to sing songs.

REVIEW

7. chop	lunch	when	match	then	dish
8. ships	grabs	bricks	can't	isn't	smashed

CHALLENGE

9. sing	sting	string	spring	springing	strong

Daily Practice

Directions: Do one activity each day. Then check the box.

☐ **Build Fluency** Read the words each day by yourself and to a partner.
☐ **Mark It** Circle all the words with **ng**. Underline all the words with **nk**.
☐ **Spell It** Have a partner say each word. Write the word. Check your answer.
☐ **Write About It** Use the words to create a story. Draw a box around the words from the list that you used.

Read-Spell-Write

Directions: Write each word two times. Say each letter as you write it.

1. who _____

2. know _____

3. was _____

4. made _____

Use in Context

Directions: Complete each sentence with a word from above.
Read the finished sentences to a partner.

1. We _____ that the king can sing.

2. Jan _____ a pink hat.

3. _____ can sing this song?

4. I _____ glad to have a hot drink.

Connected Text

Directions: **Read the story. Then answer the questions.**

The Rink

Mom and I go to the rink.
I bring my pink skates.
I know we will have fun!

At the rink, we link hands.
We slide and glide.
We sing. We spin.
Mom gives me a smile.
Good job!

It was time to go.
I say, "Thank you!"
Mom says, "You made my day!"

Interact with the Text

Directions: **Mark the text.**

1. Circle all the words with nk.

2. Draw a box around the words with ng.

Directions: **Write about the text.**

3. What does the girl say to Mom? Tell a partner. Then write about it.

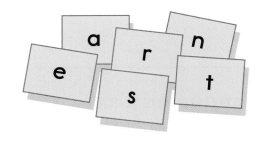

Word Sort

Sort It Out

Directions: Read each word. Then sort the words.
Write each word in the correct box.

bank	king	long	pink	ring
sink	sing	strong	thank	think

ng	nk

What did you learn about how words work?

_____

_____

_____

_____

Think and Write

Directions: Listen to each picture name.
Write the spelling for each sound in a separate box.

1.

2.

3.

Listen and Spell

Directions: Write each word and sentence that you hear.

1. _____ 2. _____

3. _____ 4. _____

5. _____

Make New Words

Directions: Make words with the letter cards on page 442.
Write the words on the lines.

e a r n
s t

_____

- - - - - - - - - - - - - -

_____

- - - - - - - - - - - - - -

_____

- - - - - - - - - - - - - -

_____

- - - - - - - - - - - - - -

_____

- - - - - - - - - - - - - -

_____

- - - - - - - - - - - - - -

_____

- - - - - - - - - - - - - -

_____

- - - - - - - - - - - - - -

Name _____

The King's Song

There once was a king
who liked to sing.
He said, "I know a song.
Will you sing along?"

1

Everyone sang the song
and tapped along.
They clapped their hands
for the king and his band!

4

2

The cook said, "Yes!"
He made pots clank.
He made cups clink
in the kitchen sink.

The maid said, "Yes!"
She made bells ring.
She made them ping
and made them ding.

3

3-Letter Blends

Directions: Say each word. Underline the 3-letter blend in the word.

1. split   **2.** stress   **3.** scrap   **4.** spring

Directions: Write a 3-letter blend from the box to complete each word.
Then write the word.

scr	spl	str	spr

5. _____ ip _____

6. _____ ang _____

7. _____ ash _____

8. _____ atch _____

Directions: Write a sentence using a word you wrote.

9. _____

Read and Write

Directions: Say each picture name. Circle the word for the picture.
Write it on the line.

kick

king

sink

1. _____

skunk

sling

trunk

2. _____

sink

sting

swing

3. _____

back

bank

tank

4. _____

inch

ink

itch

5. _____

ring

wing

wink

6. _____

Build Fluency

Directions: Complete each sentence. Use at least one word with ng or nk.

1. We made _____.

2. She was _____.

3. Who is _____?

4. I know _____.

Directions: Write a sentence using each word pair.

5. | bring, think | _____

6. | song, this | _____

Word Ladder

Directions: Listen to each clue. Then write the word.
Start at the bottom and climb to the top.

Try to save money
in this.
Change one letter.

_____ _____ _____ _____

Fish can live in this.
Change two letters.

_____ _____ _____ _____

To close and then open
one eye
Change one letter.

_____ _____ _____ _____

A bird uses this to fly.
Change one letter.

_____ _____ _____ _____

He lives with a queen.
Change one letter.

_____ _____ _____ _____

Start �

s   i   n   g

Write About It

Directions: Read "The King's Song" again.
Write what you learned about the king who likes to sing.

Fluency Check

Directions: Listen to the child read the word list. Mark one check in the green box if the word is read correctly (accuracy). Mark another check in the blue box if it is read automatically (fluency).

CUMULATIVE ASSESSMENT							
Lesson	**Word**			**Lesson**	**Word**		
11	long	☐	☐	**8**	grass	☐	☐
	bank	☐	☐		brick	☐	☐
	sunk	☐	☐		crop	☐	☐
	string	☐	☐		can't	☐	☐
10	chip	☐	☐	**7**	snap	☐	☐
	when	☐	☐		stem	☐	☐
	bunch	☐	☐		spend	☐	☐
	matching	☐	☐		skin	☐	☐
9	shop	☐	☐	**6**	clip	☐	☐
	wished	☐	☐		flap	☐	☐
	thin	☐	☐		block	☐	☐
	bath	☐	☐		glad	☐	☐

Number Correct (accuracy): _____ / 24

Number Automatic (fluency): _____ / 24

Dear Family,

Home Connection

In this unit, your child will learn about words that contain long vowels spelled with a final **e**. He or she will learn to read words with the spelling patterns of **a_e**, **i_e**, **o_e**, **u_e**, and **e_e**, such as **bake**; **time**; **pole**; **cube**; and **these**.

Read Connected Text

For each week's lesson, your child will read a Take-Home Book that focuses on the lesson skills. At week's end, the book will be sent home with your child. Read the book to your child, or read it aloud together, pointing to each word as you say it. Multiple readings will give your child practice with the lesson skills.

Practice with the Take-Home Book

Ask your child to point to words in the story that include the final **e** spelling . Have your child tell you about the book in one sentence. Write what your child says and read the description aloud together.

Lesson Skills and Take-Home Books

Lesson 12 a_e, i_e: "The Big Race"
Lesson 13 o_e, u_e, e_e: "Let's Bake a Cake!"

Extend the Learning

With your child, look for words with a final **e** in books, signs, magazine covers, etc. Keep a notebook of words you discover. Challenge your child to identify objects in your home or other locations that are spelled with a final **e**. For example, "I spy a cake."

 Visit SadlierConnect.com for **Student & Family Resources.**

Conexión con el Hogar

Apreciada familia:

En esta unidad, su niño(a) aprenderá acerca de palabras con vocales con sonidos largos y deletreadas con una **e** al final. Aprenderá a leer palabras deletreadas con los patrones **a_e**, **i_e**, **o_e**, **u_e** y **e_e**, como **bake**; **time**; **pole**; **cube** y **these**.

Leyendo la historieta en el Take-Home Book

Para cada lección de la semana su niño(a) leerá un cuadernillo de historietas, Take-Home Book, que se enfoca en las destrezas de la lección. Al final de cada semana su niño(a) llevará el cuadernillo a la casa. Lea la historieta a su niño(a) o leánla en voz alta juntos, señalando cada palabra al decirla. Leer varias veces ayudará a su niño(a) a practicar las destrezas de la lección.

Practicando con el Take-Home Book

Pida a su niño(a) señalar palabras en la historieta deletreadas con una e al final para esa lección. Luego pídale que resuma la historieta en una frase. Escriba lo que dice su niño(a) y lean juntos lo que escribió.

Lesson Skills and Take-Home Books

Lesson 12 **a_e**, **i_e**: "The Big Race"
Lesson 13 **o_e**, **u_e**, **e_e**: "Let's Bake a Cake!"

Ampliando el aprendizaje

Con su niño(a) busque palabras con una **e** al final en libros, letreros, portadas de revistas, etc. Haga una libreta con palabras que descubran juntos. Rete a su niño(a) a identificar, ya sea en su casa o en otros lugares, objetos que se deletrean con una **e** al final. Por ejemplo: "I spy a cake."

 Visite SadlierConnect.com **para recursos para el estudiante y la familia.**

Learn and Blend

Directions: Listen and join in.

A as in skate.

I as in ice.

Time for fun is always nice.

Final e

a_e   i_e

Blend It

Directions: Chorally read the words.

INTRODUCE

1. hat	hate	tap	tape	bit	bite
2. bake	take	cake	hide	side	slide
3. cake	came	made	make	bite	bike
4. game	race	page	time	smile	price

5. Jane came over to skate with us.

6. Mike likes to ride his bike.

REVIEW

7. sing	catch	bank	when	which	lunch
8. spring	flip	stop	brick	grass	clap

CHALLENGE

9. tapping   taping   backing   baking   shaking   liking

Daily Practice

Directions: Do one activity each day. Then check the box.

☐ Build Fluency Read the words each day by yourself and to a partner.

☐ Mark It Circle all the words with long a. Underline all the words with long i.

☐ Spell It Have a partner say each word. Write the word. Check your answer.

☐ Write About It Use the words to create a story. Draw a box around the words from the list that you used.

Read-Spell-Write

Directions: Write each word two times. Say each letter as you write it.

1. water _____

2. that _____

3. of _____

4. carry _____

Use in Context

Directions: Complete each sentence with a word from above.
Read the finished sentences to a partner.

1. _____ slide is wet from rain.

2. Fill the tub with _____.

3. Can Jake _____ five jugs?

4. I take a bite _____ the plum.

Connected Text

Directions: **Read the story. Then answer the questions.**

The Plane Ride

Kate smiles. She and Dad are not late.
It's five o'clock.
Time to take a plane ride!
Kate has a bottle of water to carry.

On the plane, Dad and Kate sit side-by-side.
They make a game.
What is that? A lake!
It looks like a face!

At nine o'clock, the plane lands.
Kate and Dad get off. They see Mom and wave.
Kate tells Mom about the plane ride.

Interact with the Text

Directions: **Mark the text.**

1. Circle all the words with long a.

2. Draw a box around the words with long i.

Directions: **Write about the text.**

3. What time does the plane land? Tell a partner. Then write about it.

Sort It Out

Directions: Read each word. Then sort the words. Write each word in the correct box.

bit	bite	can	cane	cap
cape	hate	hid	hide	this

a_e

short a

i_e

short i

What did you learn about how words work?

_____

- - - - - - - - - - - - - - - - - -

_____

Think and Write

Directions: Listen to each picture name.
Write the spelling for each sound in a separate box.

1.

2.

3.

Listen and Spell

Directions: Write each word and sentence that you hear.

1. _____   **2.** _____

3. _____   **4.** _____

5. _____

Make New Words

Directions: Make words with the letter cards on page 442.
Write the words on the lines.

Name

The Big Race

1

Mike has a bike.

He likes to ride it.

Up, up, up . . . and down
he rides!

They ride up and down.

Mike and Dave are fast.

They ride to the lake.

"We win!" they yell.

"Time for a picnic!"

4

2

Mike sees Dave.
"Is that bike new?" he asks.
"Yes, and it is fast, too!"
"We can have a race. It's lots
of fun!"

3

Mike and Dave make a plan.
"I will bring water," says Mike.
"And I can carry snacks,"
says Dave.
"We can race to the lake!"

Soft c and Soft g

Directions: Say each picture name. Write ace, age, or ice to complete the picture name. Write the name on the line.

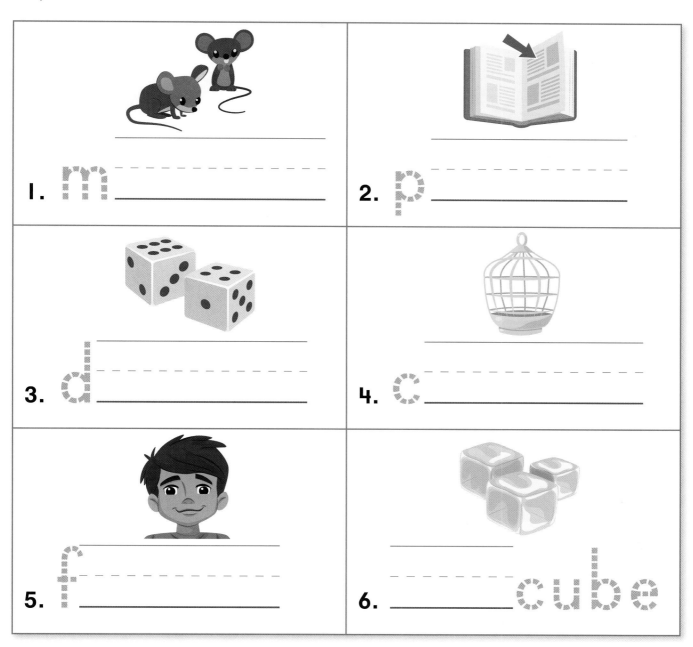

1. m _____

2. p _____

3. d _____

4. c _____

5. f _____

6. _____ cube

Directions: Write a sentence using one of the words above.

7. _____

Read and Write

Directions: Say each picture name. Circle the word for the picture.
Write it on the line.

1.
dive
nine
vine

2.
cane
game
gate

3.
skate
slide
snake

4.
fire
five
hive

5.
cake
cape
cave

6.
bake
bike
rake

Build Fluency

Directions: Complete each sentence. Use at least one word with a_e or i_e.

1. Please carry _____.

2. That is _____.

3. We eat _____.

4. I gave _____.

Directions: Write a sentence using each word pair.

5. | bike, shop |

6. | race, time |

Word Ladder

Directions: Listen to each clue. Then write the word.
Start at the bottom and climb to the top.

A clock helps you to know this.

Change two letters.

_____   _____   _____   _____

It is the past tense of "come."

Change one letter.

_____   _____   _____   _____

You might eat this on your birthday.

Change one letter.

_____   _____   _____   _____

You use the oven to do this.

Change one letter.

_____   _____   _____   _____

It has two wheels.

Change one letter.

_____   _____   _____   _____

Start →   l   i   k   e

Write About It

Directions: Read "The Big Race" again.
Write what you learned about the bike race.

Fluency Check

Directions: Listen to the child read the word list. Mark one check in the green box if the word is read correctly (accuracy). Mark another check in the blue box if it is read automatically (fluency).

Lesson	Word			Lesson	Word		
12	bake	☐	☐	9	shop	☐	☐
	side	☐	☐		wished	☐	☐
	place	☐	☐		thin	☐	☐
	fine	☐	☐		bath	☐	☐
11	long	☐	☐	8	grass	☐	☐
	bank	☐	☐		brick	☐	☐
	sunk	☐	☐		crop	☐	☐
	string	☐	☐		can't	☐	☐
10	chip	☐	☐	7	snap	☐	☐
	when	☐	☐		stem	☐	☐
	bunch	☐	☐		spend	☐	☐
	matching	☐	☐		skin	☐	☐

CUMULATIVE ASSESSMENT

Number Correct (accuracy): _____ /24

Number Automatic (fluency): _____ /24

Learn and Blend

Directions: **Listen and join in.**

E as in Pete.
U as in use.
O as in nose, close,
and those.

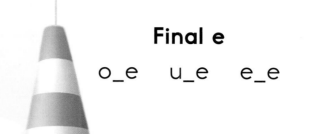

Final e

o_e   u_e   e_e

Blend It

Directions: **Chorally read the words.**

INTRODUCE

1. hop	hope	not	note	hug	huge
2. hole	pole	bone	cone	joke	broke
3. cute	cube	home	hope	robe	rode
4. use	nose	cube	rope	stone	these

5. Eve broke the vase.

6. Pete hopes you like his joke.

REVIEW

7. bike	came	ring	think	which	wish
8. shop	chips	smile	gave	send	nest

CHALLENGE

9. come	some	give	live	love	gone

Daily Practice

Directions: **Do one activity each day. Then check the box.**

☐ Build Fluency Read the words each day by yourself and to a partner.

☐ Mark It Circle all the words with long o. Underline all the words with long u.

☐ Spell It Have a partner say each word. Write the word. Check your answer.

☐ Write About It Use the words to create a story. Draw a box around the words from the list that you used.

Read-Spell-Write

Directions: Write each word two times. Say each letter as you write it.

1. use _____

2. put _____

3. don't _____

4. other _____

Use in Context

Directions: Complete each sentence with a word from above. Read the finished sentences to a partner.

1. They _____ know that joke.

2. _____ tape to fix the rip.

3. I will _____ a note on his desk.

4. What _____ wish did Steve make?

Connected Text

Directions: **Read the poem. Then answer the questions.**

My Garden

My garden at home
has a red rose.
To give it water,
I use a green hose.

My garden at home
has a big hole.
My dog uses it to keep bones
and other things that he stole!

My garden at home
has a wide, flat stone.
I put it there to sit
when I want to be alone.

Interact with the Text

Directions: **Mark the text.**

1. Circle all the words with long o.
2. Draw a box around the word that rhymes with fuse.

Directions: **Write about the text.**

3. What color is the hose? Tell a partner. Then write about it.

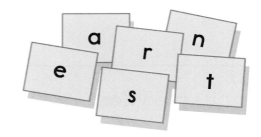

Word Sort

Sort It Out

Directions: Read each word. Then sort the words.
Write each word in the correct box.

| bone | cube | cute | home | hope |
| Steve | these | those | use | vote |

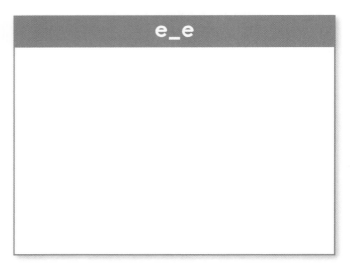

o_e

e_e

u_e

What did you learn about how words work?

_____

- -

_____

Think and Write

Directions: Listen to each picture name.
Write the spelling for each sound in a separate box.

1.

2.

3.

Listen and Spell

Directions: Write each word and sentence that you hear.

1. _____

2. _____

3. _____

4. _____

5. _____

Make New Words

Directions: Make words with the letter cards on page 444.
Write the words on the lines.

Name _____

Let's Bake a Cake!

Baking a cake at home can be fun!

Get these things: six eggs, flour, milk, and other things.

1

Take out the cake.

It is huge! It smells good.

Take a big bite. Yum!

It tastes good, too!

4

2

Melt butter on the stove.
Your mom can help.
Then mix all the ingredients.
Use a big spoon. Mix. Mix. Mix!

Put the cake in the pan.
Don't spill it!
Put the pan in the oven.
Watch it bake. And hope for
the best!

3

Inflectional Ending **ing** and **ed**

Directions: In each word, cross out the final e and add ing to make a new word. Then write the new word.

1. bake _____

2. wipe _____

3. skate _____

Directions: In each word, cross out the final e and add ed to make a new word. Then write the new word.

4. race _____

5. smile _____

Directions: Complete each sentence with a word you wrote.

6. I am _____ on the pond.

7. They _____ to the back of the line.

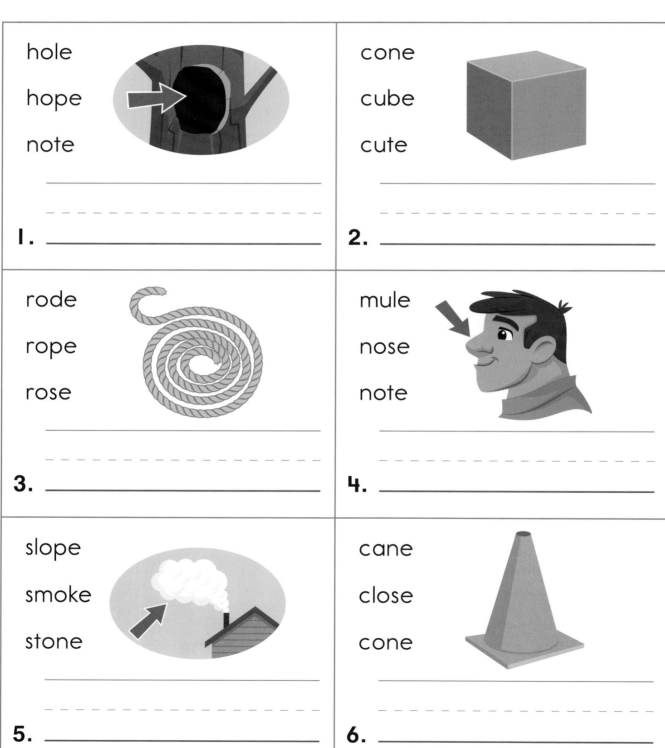

Read and Write

Directions: Say each picture name. Circle the word for the picture. Write it on the line.

1.
hole
hope
note

2.
cone
cube
cute

3.
rode
rope
rose

4.
mule
nose
note

5.
slope
smoke
stone

6.
cane
close
cone

Build Fluency

Directions: Complete each sentence. Use at least one word
with o_e, u_e, or e_e.

1. Don't _____.

2. Use the _____.

3. Put the _____.

4. The other _____.

Directions: Write a sentence using each word pair.

5. | rose, these | _____ |

6. | cone, use | _____ |

Word Ladder

Directions: Listen to each clue. Then write the word.
Start at the bottom and climb to the top.

Leaves stacked high
form into this.
Change one letter.

_____ _____ _____ _____

A skier holds one in
each hand.
Change one letter.

_____ _____ _____ _____

What an animal may dig
in your yard
Change one letter.

_____ _____ _____ _____

A place where a family
lives
Change one letter.

_____ _____ _____ _____

To want something to
happen
Add one letter.

_____ _____ _____ _____

Start ➞

h o p

Write About It

Directions: **Read "Let's Bake a Cake!" again.
Write what you learned about baking a cake.**

Fluency Check

Directions: Listen to the child read the word list. Mark one check in the green box if the word is read correctly (accuracy). Mark another check in the blue box if it is read automatically (fluency).

CUMULATIVE ASSESSMENT							
Lesson	**Word**			**Lesson**	**Word**		
13	rope	☐	☐	**10**	chip	☐	☐
	hoping	☐	☐		when	☐	☐
	these	☐	☐		bunch	☐	☐
	huge	☐	☐		matching	☐	☐
12	bake	☐	☐	**9**	shop	☐	☐
	side	☐	☐		wished	☐	☐
	place	☐	☐		thin	☐	☐
	fine	☐	☐		bath	☐	☐
11	long	☐	☐	**8**	grass	☐	☐
	bank	☐	☐		brick	☐	☐
	sunk	☐	☐		crop	☐	☐
	string	☐	☐		can't	☐	☐

Number Correct (accuracy): _____ /24

Number Automatic (fluency): _____ /24

Dear Family,

In this unit, your child will learn about words that contain long vowels. He or she will learn to read words with the long **a, i, o, u,** and **e** sounds, such as **day, rain; fly, high; go, boat, show; few, cue; team, we** and **seen.**

Read Connected Text

For each week's lesson, your child will read a Take-Home Book that focuses on the lesson skills. At week's end, the book will be sent home with your child. Read the book to your child, or read it aloud together, pointing to each word as you say it. Multiple readings will give your child practice with the lesson skills.

Practice with the Take-Home Book

Ask your child to point to words in the story with the long vowel spellings for that lesson. Have your child tell you about the book in one sentence. Write what your child says and read the description aloud together.

Lesson Skills and Take-Home Books
Lesson 14 Single-Letter Long Vowels **e, i, o:** "The New School"
Lesson 15 Long **a** (**ai, ay**): "My Big Trip"
Lesson 16 Long **e** (**ee, ea**): "The Seaside"
Lesson 17 Long **o** (**oa, ow**): "The Boat"
Lesson 18 Long **i** (**y, igh**): "The Night Sky"
Lesson 19 Long **u** (**u, ew, ue**): "Let's Make Music!"

Extend the Learning

With your child, look for words with long vowels in books, signs, magazine covers, etc. Keep a notebook of words you discover.

Challenge your child to identify objects in your home or other locations that contain long vowels. For example "I spy soap."

 Visit SadlierConnect.com **for Student & Family Resources.**

Apreciada familia:

En esta unidad, su niño(a) aprenderá acerca de palabras con vocales con sonido largo. Aprenderá a leer palabras con el sonido largo de la **a**, de la **i**, de la **o**, de la **u** y de la **e**, como **day**, **rain**; **fly**, **high**; **go**, **boat**, **show**; **few**, **cue**; **team**, **we** y **seen**.

Leyendo la historieta en el Take-Home Book

Para cada lección de la semana su niño(a) leerá un cuadernillo de historietas, Take-Home Book, que se enfoca en las destrezas de la lección. Al final de cada semana su niño(a) llevará el cuadernillo a la casa. Lea la historieta a su niño(a) o léanla en voz alta juntos, señalando cada palabra al decirla. Leer varias veces ayudará a su niño(a) a practicar las destrezas de la lección.

Practicando con el Take-Home Book

Pida a su niño(a) señalar palabras en la historieta con vocales con sonido largo para esa lección. Luego pídale que resuma la historieta en una frase. Escriba lo que dice su niño(a) y lean juntos lo que escribió.

Lesson Skills and Take-Home Books

Lesson 14 Single-Letter Long Vowels **e, i, o**: "The New School"
Lesson 15 Long **a** (**ai, ay**): "My Big Trip"
Lesson 16 Long **e** (**ee, ea**): "The Seaside"
Lesson 17 Long **o** (**oa, ow**): "The Boat"
Lesson 18 Long **i** (**y, igh**): "The Night Sky"
Lesson 19 Long **u** (**u, ew, ue**): "Let's Make Music"

Ampliando el aprendizaje

Con su niño(a) busque palabras con vocales con sonido largo en libros, letreros, portadas de revistas, etc. Haga una libreta con palabras que descubran juntos.

Rete a su niño(a) a identificar, ya sea en su casa o en otros lugares, objetos con vocales con sonido largo. Por ejemplo: "I spy soap."

 Visite SadlierConnect.com **para recursos para el estudiante y la familia.**

Learn and Blend

Directions: Listen and join in.

E as in we.
I as in hi.
O as in so, go, and no.

Single Letter Long Vowels

e   i   o

Blend It

Directions: Chorally read the words.

INTRODUCE

1. not	no	got	go	hit	hi
2. we	me	she	go	so	no

3. He will go to school.

4. We will not be at home.

REVIEW

5. clock	slip	home	lake	huge	race
6. ship	lunch	strip	bath	when	nice

CHALLENGE

7. go	going	be	begin	we	we'll

Daily Practice

Directions: Do one activity each day. Then check the box.

☐ Build Fluency Read the words each day by yourself and to a partner.

☐ Mark It Circle all the words with long o. Underline all the words with long e.

☐ Spell It Have a partner say each word. Write the word. Check your answer.

☐ Write About It Use the words to create a story. Draw a box around the words from the list that you used.

Read-Spell-Write

Directions: Write each word two times. Say each letter as you write it.

1. new _____

2. why _____

3. school _____

4. friend _____

Use in Context

Directions: Complete each sentence with a word from above.
Read the finished sentences to a partner.

1. My _____ likes to go fast.

2. Will you be late for _____?

3. _____ did she use so much milk?

4. Mom gave me a _____ bike.

Connected Text

Directions: **Read the story. Then answer the questions.**

Bo's First Day

It is Bo's first day at school.
He makes a new friend.
But she is not going to talk to him.
She is not going to send him notes.
Why not?
Bo goes to dog school!
Bo and his new friend will learn to go on walks.
They will both learn the word "no."
They will learn to be good dogs!

Interact with the Text

Directions: **Mark the text.**

1. Circle all the words that rhyme with we.

2. Draw a box around the words that rhyme with so.

Directions: **Write about the text.**

3. What will Bo learn at school? Tell a partner. Then write about it.

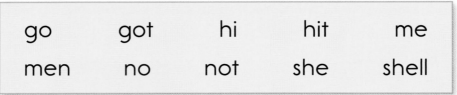

Sort It Out

Directions: Read each word. Then sort the words by vowel sound. Write each word in the correct box.

go	got	hi	hit	me
men	no	not	she	shell

Short Vowel	Long Vowel

What did you learn about how words work?

_____

- -

_____

Think and Write

Directions: Listen to each word. Write the spelling for each sound in a separate box. Then write the word on the line.

1.
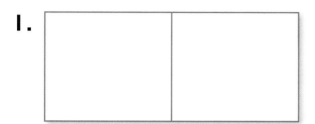

2.

3.

Listen and Spell

Directions: Write each word and sentence that you hear.

1.

2.

3.

4.

Make New Words

Directions: Make words with the letter cards on page 444.
Write the words on the lines.

1

Name _____

The New School

Jill is going to a new school.

She has no friends there.

"Will I make new friends?" she asks.

"If you say hi," says Mom.

School ends.

"I go home on the bus," says Jill.

"Me too," say the girl and boy.

"We can sit together!"

4

2

Jill sees a girl.

"Why don't you sit with me?"
she says.

"We can have so much fun."

Jill makes a new friend.

Jill sees a boy.

"Why don't you read with
me?" he says.

"We can have so much fun."

Jill makes a new friend.

3

Prefixes (re, un)

Directions: Add re to each word to make a new word. Then write the new word.

1. _____use _____

2. _____tell _____

Directions: Complete each sentence with a word you wrote.

3. I _____ the tale to my friend.

4. I will _____ my glass.

Directions: Add un to each word to make a new word. Then write the new word.

1. _____lock _____

2. _____ripe _____

Directions: Complete each sentence with a word you wrote.

3. This plum is _____.

4. Who will _____ the box?

Read and Write

Directions: Read each word. Circle the word that has a long vowel sound.
Then write the word on the line.

1.	be _____ bed - - - - - bet _____		**2.**	net _____ no - - - - - not _____	
3.	so _____ sock - - - - - stop _____		**4.**	set _____ she - - - - - shell _____	
5.	hi _____ hill - - - - - hit _____		**6.**	he _____ help - - - - - hen _____	

What is the same about all the words you circled?

_____

_____

Build Fluency

Directions: Complete each sentence. Use at least one word with long vowel e, i, or o.

1. The water _____.

2. My friend _____.

3. Please don't _____.

4. Why is _____?

Directions: Write a sentence using each word pair.

5. | go, when | _____

6. | me, sang | _____

Word Ladder

Directions: Listen to each clue. Then write the word.
Start at the bottom and climb to the top.

You say this when you meet someone.
Change one letter.

_____ _____

Not "she"
Take away one letter.

_____ _____

Not "he"
Take away one letter.
Add two letters.

_____ _____ _____

Not "you"
Change one letter.

_____ _____

You and I
Take away one letter.

_____ _____

Start ➔   w e t

Write About It

Directions: Read "The New School" again.
Write what you learned about Jill.

Fluency Check

Directions: Listen to the child read the word list. Mark one check in the green box if the word is read correctly (accuracy). Mark another check in the blue box if it is read automatically (fluency).

CUMULATIVE ASSESSMENT

Lesson	Word			Lesson	Word		
14	we	☐	☐	11	long	☐	☐
	hi	☐	☐		bank	☐	☐
	go	☐	☐		sunk	☐	☐
	she	☐	☐		string	☐	☐
13	rope	☐	☐	10	chip	☐	☐
	hoping	☐	☐		when	☐	☐
	these	☐	☐		bunch	☐	☐
	huge	☐	☐		matching	☐	☐
12	bake	☐	☐	9	shop	☐	☐
	side	☐	☐		wished	☐	☐
	place	☐	☐		thin	☐	☐
	fine	☐	☐		bath	☐	☐

Number Correct (accuracy): _____ /24

Number Automatic (fluency): _____ /24

Learn and Blend

Directions: Listen and join in.

A as in ant.
A as in late.
A as in apron, pay,
and wait.

Long a

a   ai

ay   a_e

Blend It

Directions: Chorally read the words.

INTRODUCE

1. ran	rain	plan	plain	sad	say
2. may	pay	play	say	stay	stray
3. pail	sail	tail	trail	train	brain
4. chain	tray	faint	nail	paint	raise

5. "Rain, rain, go away," yelled Gail.

6. I had to wait all day for the train to come.

REVIEW

7. go	she	hope	cute	ride	same
8. bring	ranch	chop	sink	pitch	when

CHALLENGE

9. rain   rainbow   day   birthday

Daily Practice

Directions: Do one activity each day. Then check the box.

☐ **Build Fluency** Read the words each day by yourself and to a partner.

☐ **Mark It** Circle all the words with ai. Underline all the words with ay.

☐ **Spell It** Have a partner say each word. Write the word. Check your answer.

☐ **Write About It** Use the words to create a story. Draw a box around the words from the list that you used.

Read-Spell-Write

Directions: Write each word two times. Say each letter as you write it.

1. away

2. one

3. doesn't

4. something

Use in Context

Directions: Complete each sentence with a word from above.
Read the finished sentences to a partner.

1. My dog _____ like to play catch.

2. _____ big is inside that box.

3. _____ day I will ride in a train.

4. "Go _____ !" yelled Kate.

Connected Text

Directions: **Read the clues. Then answer the questions.**

What Will I Paint?

1. I will paint something big.
It runs on tracks all day.
It goes fast. You may ride it if you pay.
What will I paint?   (train)

2. I will paint something wet.
It is in the big gray clouds.
When it comes down, you may stay inside.
What will I paint?   (rain)

3. I will paint an animal. It has a little shell.
It doesn't go fast.
What will I paint?   (snail)

Interact with the Text

Directions: **Mark the text.**

1. Circle all the words with long a spellings.

2. Draw a box around the words that rhyme with say.

Directions: **Write about the text.**

3. What did the child paint? Tell a partner. Then write about it.

_____

_ _

_____

Word Sort

Sort It Out

Directions: Read each word. Then sort the words.
Write each word in the correct box.

gray	may	nail	paint	play
rain	sail	say	stay	train

ai	ay

What did you learn about how words work?

_____

- -

_____

Think and Write

Directions: Listen to each picture name.
Write the spelling for each sound in a separate box.

1.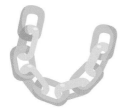

2.

3.

Listen and Spell

Directions: Write each word and sentence that you hear.

1. _____

2. _____

3. _____

4. _____

5. _____

Make New Words

Directions: Make words with the letter cards on page 444.
Write the words on the lines.

Name _____

My Big Trip

Last May, I went to Spain.

It was a fun trip.

What did I do there?

Take a look!

1

Spain is a fun place to visit.

When I go away next spring, maybe I will go back.

But I hope it doesn't rain again!

4

LIBROS

2

One day, I rode in a train.

I paid a lot for the ride.

I went to see a museum.

I had to wait in a long line to get inside.

The next day, it rained.

I went to see a castle.

A castle is a big home for a king and queen.

But the King of Spain doesn't live in this one.

3

Compound Words

Directions: Write the name of each picture. Use the words in the box. Then combine the picture names to make a compound word. Draw a picture above the word you made.

brush	rain	foot	tooth	box	ball	mail	bow

1. _____ + _____ = _____

2. _____ + _____ = _____

3. _____ + _____ = _____

4. _____ + _____ = _____

Read and Write

Directions: Say each picture name. Circle the word for the picture.
Write it on the line.

chain
train
tray

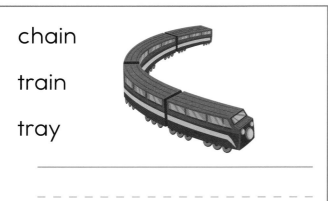

1. _____

sail
small
snail

2. _____

grain
grade
gray

3. _____

pain
paint
pants

4. _____

spray
stay
stray

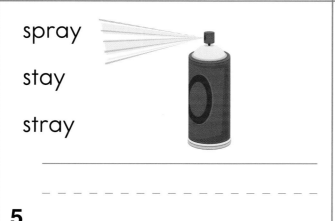

5. _____

pay
plane
play

6. _____

Build Fluency

Directions: Complete each sentence. Use at least one word with ai or ay.

1. He doesn't _____.

2. Who will _____?

3. My school _____.

4. Don't use _____.

Directions: Write a sentence using each word pair.

5. race, snail

6. hope, stay

Word Ladder

Directions: Listen to each clue. Then write the word.
Start at the bottom and climb to the top.

A color
Add one letter.

_____ _____ _____ _____

A beam of light
Change one letter.

_____ _____ _____

Past tense of "run"
Take away one letter.

_____ _____ _____

It falls from the clouds.
Take away one letter.

_____ _____ _____ _____

This runs on a track. Choo choo!
Change one letter.

_____ _____ _____ _____

Start ➔ g r a i n

Write About It

Directions: Read "My Big Trip" again.
Write what you learned about Spain.

Fluency Check

Directions: Listen to the child read the word list. Mark one check in the green box if the word is read correctly (accuracy). Mark another check in the blue box if it is read automatically (fluency).

Lesson	Word			Lesson	Word		
15	brain	☐	☐	12	bake	☐	☐
	gray	☐	☐		side	☐	☐
	sway	☐	☐		place	☐	☐
	paintbrush	☐	☐		fine	☐	☐
14	we	☐	☐	11	long	☐	☐
	hi	☐	☐		bank	☐	☐
	go	☐	☐		sunk	☐	☐
	she	☐	☐		string	☐	☐
13	rope	☐	☐	10	chip	☐	☐
	hoping	☐	☐		when	☐	☐
	these	☐	☐		bunch	☐	☐
	huge	☐	☐		matching	☐	☐

CUMULATIVE ASSESSMENT

Number Correct (accuracy): _____ /24

Number Automatic (fluency): _____ /24

Learn and Blend

Directions: Listen and join in.

E as in egg.
E as in eat.
E as in these, me,
and feet.

Long e

e   ee

ea   e_e

Blend It

Directions: Chorally read the words.

INTRODUCE

1. met   meat   red   read   sat   seat

2. bean   mean   heat   neat   feed   seed

3. meal   mean   beach   beat   green   greet

4. sleep   teeth   speed   dream   please   clean

5. We see a seal on the beach.

6. We like to eat peaches and ice cream.

REVIEW

7. brain   play   she   go   nose   cute

8. huge   smile   game   which   fish   lunch

CHALLENGE

9. teachers maybe cleaned seedless reading mealtime

Daily Practice

Directions: Do one activity each day. Then check the box.

☐ **Build Fluency** Read the words each day by yourself and to a partner.

☐ **Mark It** Circle all the words with **ee**. Underline all the words with **ea**.

☐ **Spell It** Have a partner say each word. Write the word. Check your answer.

☐ **Write About It** Use the words to create a story. Draw a box around the words from the list that you used.

Read-Spell-Write

Directions: Write each word two times. Say each letter as you write it.

1. find

2. around

3. under

4. wash

Use in Context

Directions: Complete each sentence with a word from above.
Read the finished sentences to a partner.

1. Please help me _____ my truck.

2. Did she _____ each dish?

3. The fish swim _____ the rock.

4. She sat _____ the tree to read.

Connected Text

Directions: **Read the poem. Then answer the questions.**

Good Deeds

I do good deeds.
I help my friends with all their needs.

Jean is new and needs a seat.
I help her find one next to Pete.

Lee makes a mess. We wash and clean.
I help a lot. I am not mean.

I do good deeds.
I help my friends with all their needs.

Interact with the Text

Directions: **Mark the text.**

1. Circle all the words with long e.

2. Draw a box around the words that rhyme with mean.

Directions: **Write about the text.**

3. What does the child find for Jean? Tell a partner. Then write about it.

Word Sort

Sort It Out

Directions: Read each word. Then sort the words.
Write each word in the correct box.

| clean | meat | need | peach | queen |
| seed | sleep | speak | tea | week |

ee	ea

What did you learn about how words work?

_____

- -

_____

228   Long e • Lesson 16

Think and Write

Directions: Listen to each picture name.
Write the spelling for each sound in a separate box.

1.

2.

3.

Listen and Spell

Directions: Write each word and sentence that you hear.

1. _____

2. _____

3. _____

4. _____

5. _____

Make New Words

Directions: Make words with the letter cards on page 444.
Write the words on the lines.

_____

- - - - - - - - - - - - - - - - -

_____

_____

- - - - - - - - - - - - - - - - -

_____

_____

- - - - - - - - - - - - - - - - -

_____

_____

- - - - - - - - - - - - - - - - -

_____

_____

- - - - - - - - - - - - - - - - -

_____

Name _____

The Seaside

Go to the seaside.
What do you see?
You see a beach with sand
all around.

1

Go to the seaside.
What do you find?
You find cans and bags, so
you clean up the beach.

4

2

Go to the seaside.
What do you do?
You pick up seashells, then
wash off the green seaweed.

Fold   Fold

Go to the seaside.
What do you feel?
You feel the heat on your
head and on the sand under
your feet.

3

Short **e** Spelled **ea**

Directions: **Read each word. Circle the words with the short e sound.
Then complete each sentence with the correct word.**

bean	bread	head	meal
seal	seat	speak	thread

1. I ate a slice of _____.

2. I saw a _____ at the zoo.

3. The _____ is green.

4. I have a hat on my _____.

5. I sat on the _____.

Directions: **Write a word from the box above that rhymes with each word below.**

6. red _____

7. seen _____

Read and Write

Directions: Say each picture name. Circle the word for the picture. Write it on the line.

beach
beat
peach

1. _____

feed
feet
free

2. _____

lead
leaf
leap

3. _____

dream
steam
team

4. _____

teach
teeth
treat

5. _____

sheep
sleep
speak

6. _____

Build Fluency

Directions: Complete each sentence. Use at least one word with ee or ea.

1. I see _____.

2. Sit under _____.

3. He doesn't _____.

4. Our new _____.

Directions: Write a sentence using each word pair.

5. green, paint _____

6. clean, home _____

Word Ladder

Directions: Listen to each clue. Then write the word.
Start at the bottom and climb to the top.

This can be part of a necklace.
Add one letter.

_____ _____ _____ _____

You put your pillow on this.
Change one letter.

_____ _____ _____

It is the past tense of "feed."
Take away one letter.

_____ _____ _____ _____

You do this when you give food to your pet.
Change one letter.

_____ _____ _____ _____ _____

Plant this in soil.
Add one letter.

_____ _____ _____ _____ _____

Start ➔   s   e   e

Write About It

Directions: Read "The Seaside" again.
Write what you learned about visiting the seaside.

Fluency Check

Directions: Listen to the child read the word list. Mark one check in the green box if the word is read correctly (accuracy). Mark another check in the blue box if it is read automatically (fluency).

Lesson	Word			Lesson	Word		
16	bean	☐	☐	13	rope	☐	☐
	reading	☐	☐		hoping	☐	☐
	seeds	☐	☐		these	☐	☐
	needed	☐	☐		huge	☐	☐
15	brain	☐	☐	12	bake	☐	☐
	gray	☐	☐		side	☐	☐
	sway	☐	☐		place	☐	☐
	paintbrush	☐	☐		fine	☐	☐
14	we	☐	☐	11	long	☐	☐
	hi	☐	☐		bank	☐	☐
	go	☐	☐		sunk	☐	☐
	she	☐	☐		string	☐	☐

CUMULATIVE ASSESSMENT

Number Correct (accuracy): _____ /24

Number Automatic (fluency): _____ /24

238   **Long e • Lesson 16**

Learn and Blend

Directions: Listen and join in.

O as in on.
O as in coat.
O as in go, row, and vote.

Long o

o	oa
ow	o_e

Blend It

Directions: Chorally read the words.

INTRODUCE

1.	cot	coat	bat	boat	go	grow
2.	road	toad	goat	throat	coast	toast
3.	low	flow	glow	grow	snow	slow
4.	foam	show	loaf	float	blow	row

5. The slow boat floated down the river.

6. Did you hear that toad croak?

REVIEW

7.	train	stay	plate	bike	main	cute
8.	hope	tray	mile	paint	green	street

CHALLENGE

9. soaking   floating   showing   snowing   loading   growing

Daily Practice

Directions: Do one activity each day. Then check the box.

☐ **Build Fluency** Read the words each day by yourself and to a partner.

☐ **Mark It** Circle all the words with **oa**. Underline all the words with **ow**.

☐ **Spell It** Have a partner say each word. Write the word. Check your answer.

☐ **Write About It** Use the words to create a story. Draw a box around the words from the list that you used.

Read-Spell-Write

Directions: Write each word two times. Say each letter as you write it.

1. part _____

2. people _____

3. more _____

4. or _____

Use in Context

Directions: Complete each sentence with a word from above.
Read the finished sentences to a partner.

1. I will make _____ toast to eat.

2. Is that a frog _____ a toad?

3. I read this _____ of the page.

4. Many _____ grow green beans.

Connected Text

Directions: **Read the story. Then answer the questions.**

Let's Go Camping

Let's go camping.

First, we'll pack.

We'll need a tent and some rope,

And some marshmallows or hot dogs to roast.

Don't forget to bring a coat.

What more should we pack?

I don't know. It's time to get on the road!

Interact with the Text

Directions: **Mark the text.**

1. Circle all the words with long o.

2. Draw a box around the word that rhymes with go.

Directions: **Write about the text.**

3. What are some things you need to pack? Tell a partner. Then write about it.

Word Sort

Sort It Out

Directions: Read each word. Then sort the words.
Write each word in the correct box.

boat	coach	coat	grow	know
low	road	show	snow	toast

oa	ow

What did you learn about how words work?

_____

- -

_____

Think and Write

Directions: Listen to each picture name.
Write the spelling for each sound in a separate box.

1.

2.

3.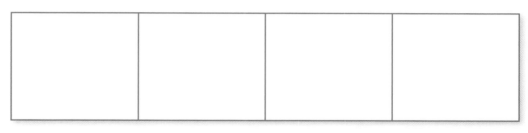

Listen and Spell

Directions: Write each word and sentence that you hear.

1. _____

2. _____

3. _____

4. _____

5. _____

Make New Words

Directions: Make words with the letter cards on page 444.
Write the words on the lines.

Name

The Boat

Joan and I row the boat.

"Watch out," says Joan. "Or we will bump into a seal."

"Do they like this part of the coast?" I ask.

People wave.

"Can you fit any more?"

"No," I say.

"We have a big load!"

And we row, row, row away.

4

2

A big toad croaks. Ribbit!
"Can I fit on your boat?"
"Yes," I say.
"It is just Joan and me."

A goat roams by.
"Can I fit on your boat?"
"Yes," I say.
"It is Toad, Joan, and me.
So, get on slowly."

3

Fold

Fold

Suffixes (ful, less)

Directions: Add ful to each word to make a new word. Then write the new word.

1. grace _____ _____

2. play _____ _____

3. help _____ _____

Directions: Add less to each word to make a new word. Then write the new word.

4. hope _____ _____

5. pain _____ _____

6. use _____ _____

Directions: Complete each sentence with a word you wrote.

7. That _____ kitten is so cute.

8. A bell that doesn't ring is _____.

Read and Write

Directions: Say each picture name. Circle the word for the picture.
Write it on the line.

boat
coat
goat

1. _____

coat
load
soak

2. _____

road
row
toad

3. _____

show
slow
snow

4. _____

bow
snow
soap

5. _____

float
roast
toast

6. _____

Build Fluency

Directions: Complete each sentence. Use at least one word
with **oa** or **ow**.

1. Have more _____.

2. Many people _____.

3. Put away _____.

4. They find _____.

Directions: Write a sentence using each word pair.

5. | grow, seed | _____

_____

6. | boat, dream | _____

_____

Word Ladder

Directions: Listen to each clue. Then write the word.
Start at the bottom and climb to the top.

Water a plant and watch it do this.

Add one letter.

_____ _____ _____ _____

Sit in a boat, hold the oars, and do this.

Change one letter.

_____ _____ _____

Wrap your gift and put this on top!

Take away two letters.
Add one letter.

_____ _____ _____

You can travel across a lake in one of these.

Change one letter.

_____ _____ _____ _____

You can wear one on a cool day.

Change one letter.

_____ _____ _____ _____

Start ➔  g o a t

Write About It

Directions: Read "The Boat" again.
Write about the group in the boat.

Fluency Check

Directions: Listen to the child read the word list. Mark one check in the green box if the word is read correctly (accuracy). Mark another check in the blue box if it is read automatically (fluency).

CUMULATIVE ASSESSMENT

Lesson	Word			Lesson	Word		
17	soap	☐	☐	**14**	we	☐	☐
	slowly	☐	☐		hi	☐	☐
	loaf	☐	☐		go	☐	☐
	flown	☐	☐		she	☐	☐
16	bean	☐	☐	**13**	rope	☐	☐
	reading	☐	☐		hoping	☐	☐
	seeds	☐	☐		these	☐	☐
	needed	☐	☐		huge	☐	☐
15	brain	☐	☐	**12**	bake	☐	☐
	gray	☐	☐		side	☐	☐
	sway	☐	☐		place	☐	☐
	paintbrush	☐	☐		fine	☐	☐

Number Correct (accuracy): _____ /24

Number Automatic (fluency): _____ /24

Learn and Blend

Directions: Listen and join in.

I as in it.
I as in my.
I as in hi, ride,
and sigh.

Long i

i	y
igh	i_e

Blend It

Directions: Chorally read the words.

INTRODUCE

1. fit	fight	lit	light	sit	sight
2. by	why	shy	spy	dry	cry
3. right	bright	night	fight	flight	tight
4. I	my	sky	high	fly	sigh

5. Did you try to fly my kite?

6. The bright light helps me read at night.

REVIEW

7. road	grow	teeth	seats	stay	raining
8. so	hi	home	use	these	bike

CHALLENGE

9. light   lightning   fight   fighter   bright   brighter

Daily Practice

Directions: Do one activity each day. Then check the box.

☐ **Build Fluency** Read the words each day by yourself and to a partner.

☐ **Mark It** Circle all the words with y. Underline all the words with igh.

☐ **Spell It** Have a partner say each word. Write the word. Check your answer.

☐ **Write About It** Use the words to create a story. Draw a box around the words from the list that you used.

Read-Spell-Write

Directions: Write each word two times. Say each letter as you write it.

1. different _____

2. full _____

3. into _____

4. through _____

Use in Context

Directions: Complete each sentence with a word from above.
Read the finished sentences to a partner.

1. We see _____ bugs at night.

2. Do not drive _____ a red light!

3. My sink is _____ of dishes.

4. Why do bats fly _____ caves?

Connected Text

Directions: **Read the "how to" list. Then answer the questions.**

How to Grow a Bean Plant

Here's how to grow a bean plant:

- Get a pot full of soil.
  You need a bean seed and water, too.

- Poke a hole in the soil.

- Drop a bean seed into the hole.
  You might want to cover it with soil.

- Water it every day. Don't let it get dry!

- Try to keep the pot by a bright window.
  A bean plant needs light to grow.

Interact with the Text

Directions: **Mark the text.**

1. Circle all the words with long i.

2. Draw a box around the words that rhyme with sight.

Directions: **Write about the text.**

3. What does a bean plant need to grow? Tell a partner. Then write about it.

Sort It Out

Directions: Read each word. Then sort the words.
Write each word in the correct box.

| bright | cry | fight | fly | might |
| my | night | right | shy | try |

y	igh

What did you learn about how words work?

_____

- -

_____

Think and Write

Directions: Listen to each picture name.
Write the spelling for each sound in a separate box.

1.

2.

3.

Listen and Spell

Directions: Write each word and sentence that you hear.

1. _____ 2. _____

3. _____ 4. _____

5. _____

Make New Words

Directions: Make words with the letter cards on page 444.
Write the words on the lines.

e a r n t s

1

Name

The Night Sky

Fold

Fold

The day is done.
The sun's light fades.
The sky gets dark.
Day turns into night.

The sky gets lighter.
The night ends.
The bats and foxes go to
sleep.
When will day turn into night?

4

2

Different stars light up the sky.
The full moon is the brightest sight.
All is right in the night sky.

Foxes look for food.
Bats fly through the sky.
Fireflies light up.
These animals like the night.

3

Comparatives and Superlatives (er, est)

Directions: Add er or est to each word. Write the new word.

er	est

1. fast

2. cold

3. soft

4. sweet

5. slow

Directions: Write two sentences. Use one of the words you wrote in each sentence.

6. _____

7. _____

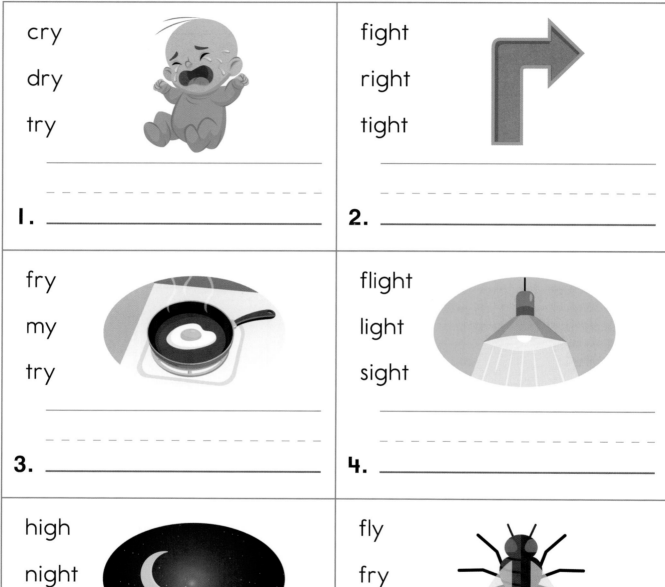

Read and Write

Directions: Say each picture name. Circle the word for the picture.
Write it on the line.

cry
dry
try

1. _____

fight
right
tight

2. _____

fry
my
try

3. _____

flight
light
sight

4. _____

high
night
tight

5. _____

fly
fry
sky

6. _____

Build Fluency

Directions: Complete each sentence. Use at least one word with y or igh.

1. Step into _____.

2. Our friend _____.

3. People like _____.

4. She doesn't _____.

Directions: Write a sentence using each word pair.

5. | coat, try |

6. | high, why |

Word Ladder

Directions: Listen to each clue. Then write the word.
Start at the bottom and climb to the top.

A person like this may
not talk much.

Change two letters.

_____ _____ _____

A baby makes this
sound.

Change one letter.

_____ _____ _____

This is a way to cook fish
in a pan.

Change one letter.

_____ _____ _____ _____

A bee has wings to
do this.

**Take away one letter.
Add two letters.**

_____ _____ _____

It rhymes with "try."

Change one letter.

_____ _____

Start →

m e

Write About It

Directions: Read "The Night Sky" again.
Write what you learned about what happens at night.

Fluency Check

Directions: Listen to the child read the word list. Mark one check in the green box if the word is read correctly (accuracy). Mark another check in the blue box if it is read automatically (fluency).

CUMULATIVE ASSESSMENT							
Lesson	**Word**			**Lesson**	**Word**		
18	try	☐	☐	**15**	brain	☐	☐
	might	☐	☐		gray	☐	☐
	brightest	☐	☐		sway	☐	☐
	flying	☐	☐		paintbrush	☐	☐
17	soap	☐	☐	**14**	we	☐	☐
	slowly	☐	☐		hi	☐	☐
	loaf	☐	☐		go	☐	☐
	flown	☐	☐		she	☐	☐
16	bean	☐	☐	**13**	rope	☐	☐
	reading	☐	☐		hoping	☐	☐
	seeds	☐	☐		these	☐	☐
	needed	☐	☐		huge	☐	☐

Number Correct (accuracy): _____ /24

Number Automatic (fluency): _____ /24

Learn and Blend

Directions: Listen and join in.

U as in cut.
U as in cute.
U as in rescue, few,
and mute.

Long u	
u	ew
ue	u_e

Blend It

Directions: Chorally read the words.

INTRODUCE

1. feel   fuel   fed   few   men   menu

2. cue   rescue   view   viewing   music   unit

3. I like to listen to rock music.

4. I need a few new pens.

REVIEW

5. night   my   bright   sky   coat   try

6. show   dream   sheep   train   gray   stone

CHALLENGE

7. beautiful   continue   music   museum   human   argue

Daily Practice

Directions: Do one activity each day. Then check the box.

☐ Build Fluency   Read the words each day by yourself and to a partner.

☐ Mark It   Circle all the words with ew. Underline all the words with ue.

☐ Spell It   Have a partner say each word. Write the word. Check your answer.

☐ Write About It   Use the words to create a story. Draw a box around the words from the list that you used.

Read-Spell-Write

Directions: Write each word two times. Say each letter as you write it.

1. could _____

2. would _____

3. their _____

4. together _____

Use in Context

Directions: Complete each sentence with a word from above.
Read the finished sentences to a partner.

1. _____ little puppy is so cute.

2. I _____ read parts of the menu.

3. We sang a few songs _____.

4. _____ you like to play with us?

Connected Text

Directions: **Read the clues. Then answer the questions.**

Where Could I Find?

1. Where could I find huge dinosaurs?
Where could I find old planes?
Where could I find these things together?

(Answer: at a museum)

2. Where could I find cute goats?
Where could I find a mule?
Where could I find these animals together?

(Answer: at a farm)

3. Where could I find a stage?
Where could I find people making music?

(Answer: at a concert)

Interact with the Text

Directions: **Mark the text.**

1. Circle all the words with long u spelled u_e.

2. Draw a box around the words with long u spelled u.

Directions: **Write about the text.**

3. Where could the goats and mule be? Tell a partner. Then write about it.

Sort It Out

Directions: Read each word. Then sort the words by vowel sound.
Write each word in the correct box.

argue	bug	cue	few	menu
music	nut	shut	stuck	value

Long u	Short u

What did you learn about how words work?

_____

- -

_____

Think and Write

Directions: Say each word. Circle the word that has the long u sound. Then write the word on the line.

1. us   use   _____

2. hug   huge   _____

3. cube   cub   _____

Listen and Spell

Directions: Write each word and sentence that you hear.

1. _____   **2.** _____

3. _____

Make New Words

Directions: Make words with the letter cards on page 446.
Write the words on the lines.

_____

- - - - - - - - - - - - - - - - -

_____

_____

- - - - - - - - - - - - - - - - -

_____

_____

- - - - - - - - - - - - - - - - -

_____

_____

- - - - - - - - - - - - - - - - -

_____

Let's Make Music!

Name _____

It is fun to make music.
Look for things to use.
You could use a pot.
Bam! Bam! You made a drum.

1

Get together with a few friends.
Have them make music.
One, two, play on cue.
That would be fun!

4

2

You made a bugle.
Puff! Puff!
Then blow into it.
You could roll up some paper.

3

You made a guitar.
Ting! Ting! Ping!
You could use a rubber band.

Compound Words

Directions: Choose a word from each box to make a compound word.
Then write the compound word.

home	some	sun

made	one	shine

1. _____ + _____ = _____

2. _____ + _____ = _____

3. _____ + _____ = _____

Directions: Write a sentence for each compound word you wrote.

4. _____

5. _____

6. _____

Read and Write

Directions: Say each picture name. Circle the word for the picture.
Write it on the line.

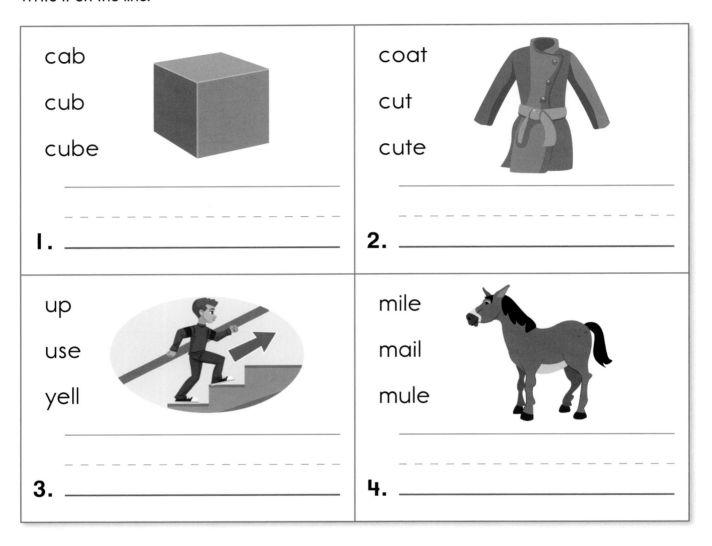

cab
cub
cube

1. _____

coat
cut
cute

2. _____

up
use
yell

3. _____

mile
mail
mule

4. _____

Directions: Circle the two words that have the long u sound.
Write the words on the lines.

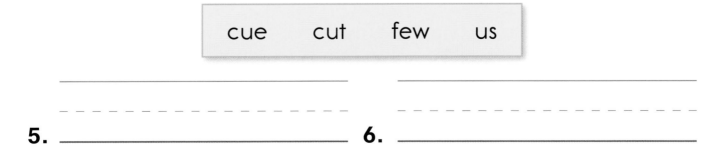

cue   cut   few   us

5. _____   6. _____

Build Fluency

Directions: Complete each sentence. Use at least one word with u, ew, or ue.

1. I'll find _____.

2. Together we _____.

3. Some people _____.

4. I could _____.

Directions: Write a sentence using each word pair.

5. | feed, my | _____

6. | few, road | _____

Word Ladder

Directions: Listen to each clue. Then write the word.
Start at the bottom and climb to the top.

This is another name for a baby bear.
Take away one letter.

_____ _____ _____

Ice in your freezer can have this shape.
Change one letter.

_____ _____ _____ _____

This word describes a sweet, loveable dog.
Add one letter.

_____ _____ _____ _____

You use scissors to do this.
Change one letter.

_____ _____ _____

This is a signal to do something.
Change one letter.

_____ _____ _____

Start ➔

c u p

Write About It

Directions: Read "Let's Make Music!" again.
Write what you learned about how you can make music.

Fluency Check

Directions: Listen to the child read the word list. Mark one check in the green box if the word is read correctly (accuracy). Mark another check in the blue box if it is read automatically (fluency).

CUMULATIVE ASSESSMENT							
Lesson	Word			Lesson	Word		
19	few	☐	☐	**16**	bean	☐	☐
	cue	☐	☐		reading	☐	☐
	menu	☐	☐		seeds	☐	☐
	music	☐	☐		needed	☐	☐
18	try	☐	☐	**15**	brain	☐	☐
	might	☐	☐		gray	☐	☐
	brightest	☐	☐		sway	☐	☐
	flying	☐	☐		paintbrush	☐	☐
17	soap	☐	☐	**14**	we	☐	☐
	slowly	☐	☐		hi	☐	☐
	loaf	☐	☐		go	☐	☐
	flown	☐	☐		she	☐	☐

Number Correct (accuracy): _____ /24

Number Automatic (fluency): _____ /24

UNIT 5

Dear Family,

Home Connection

In this unit, your child will learn about words with r-controlled vowels **ar, er, ir, ur, or, ore, oar, are, air,** and **ear,** such as **jar; fern; stir; burn; for; store; soar; share; pair;** and **pear.** He or she will learn to read words with short and long **oo** such as **spoon; could; flew; glue;** and **tune,** words with diphthongs **ou, ow, oi, oy,** such as **mouth; cow; join;** and **toy,** and words with complex vowel /ô/ spelled **au, aw, alk, alt, all,** such as **cause; raw; walk; salt;** and **ball.**

Read Connected Text

For each week's lesson, your child will read a Take-Home Book that focuses on the lesson skill. At week's end, the book will be sent home with your child. Read the book to your child, or read it aloud together, pointing to each word as you say it. Multiple readings will give your child practice with the lesson skills.

Practice with the Take-Home Book

Ask your child to point to words in the story that include the r-controlled vowels, complex vowels, or diphthongs for that lesson.

Have your child tell you about the book in one sentence. Write what your child says and read the description aloud together.

Lesson Skills and Take-Home Books

Lesson 20 r-Controlled **ar:** "On the Farm"
Lesson 21 r-Controlled **er, ir, ur:** "Pam Gets Hurt"
Lesson 22 r-Controlled **or, ore, oar:** "Stores at the Mall"
Lesson 23 Short and Long **oo:** "Books, Books, Books!"
Lesson 24 Diphthong **ou, ow:** "The Parade Is in Town!"
Lesson 25 Diphthong **oi, oy:** "Join a Club!"
Lesson 26 Complex Vowel /ô/ **au, aw, alk, alt, all:** "A Walk in the Park"
Lesson 27 r-Controlled **are, air, ear:** "The Three Bears: A Retelling"

Extend the Learning

With your child, look for words with r-controlled vowels, complex vowel /ô/, and diphthongs in books, signs, magazine covers, etc. Keep a notebook of words you discover.

Challenge your child to identify objects in your home or other locations that have r-controlled vowels, complex vowel /ô/, or diphthongs. For example, "I spy a coin."

 Visit SadlierConnect.com **for Student & Family Resources.**

Apreciada familia:

En esta unidad, su niño(a) aprenderá acerca de palabras con vocales con el sonido controlado por la r, **ar**, **er**, **ir**, **ur**, **or**, **ore**, **oar**, **are**, **air** y **ear**, como **jar**; **fern**; **stir**; **burn**; **for**; **store**; **soar**; **share**; **pair** y **pear**. Aprenderá a leer palabras con sonido **oo** corto y largo, como **spoon**; **could**; **flew**; **glue** y **tune**; con diptongos **ou**, **ow**, **oi**, **oy**, como **mouth**; **cow**; **join** y **toy**, y palabras con el sonido de la vocal compleja /ô/ deletreada **au**, **aw**, **alk**, **alt**, **all**, como **cause**; **raw**; **walk**; **salt** y **ball**.

Conexión con el Hogar

Leyendo la historieta en el Take-Home Book

Para cada lección de la semana su niño(a) leerá un cuadernillo de historietas, Take-Home Book, que se enfoca en las destrezas de la lección. Al final de cada semana su niño(a) llevará el cuadernillo a la casa. Lea la historieta a su niño(a) o leánla en voz alta juntos, señalando cada palabra al decirla. Leer varias veces ayudará a su niño(a) a practicar las destrezas de la lección.

Practicando con el Take-Home Book

Pida a su niño(a) señalar palabras en la historieta con vocales con el sonido controlado por la r, de vocales complejas o diptongos para esa lección. Luego pídale que resuma la historieta en una frase. Escriba lo que dice su niño(a) y lean juntos lo que escribió.

Lesson Skills and Take-Home Books

Lesson 20 r-Controlled **ar**: "On the Farm"
Lesson 21 r-Controlled **er**, **ir**, **ur**: "Pam Gets Hurt"
Lesson 22 r-Controlled **or**, **ore**, **ur**: "Stores at the Mall"
Lesson 23 Short and Long **oo**: "Books, Books, Books!"
Lesson 24 Diphthong **ou**, **ow**: "The Parade Is in Town!"
Lesson 25 Diphthong **oi**, **oy**: "Join a Club!"
Lesson 26 Complex Vowel /ô/ **au**, **aw**, **alk**, **alt**, **all**: "A Walk in the Park"
Lesson 27 r-Controlled **are**, **air**, **ear**: "The Three Bears: A Retelling"

Ampliando el aprendizaje

Con su niño(a) busque palabras con vocales con el sonido controlado por la r, de vocales complejas o diptongos en libros, letreros, portadas de revistas, etc. Haga una libreta con palabras que descubran juntos. Rete a su niño(a) a identificar, ya sea en su casa o en otros lugares, objetos con vocales con el sonido controlado por la r, de vocales complejas o diptongos. Por ejemplo: "I spy a coin."

 Visite SadlierConnect.com para recursos para el estudiante y la familia.

Learn and Blend

Directions: Listen and join in.

Ar as in star, start, car, and cart.

r-Controlled Vowel

ar

Blend It

Directions: Chorally read the words.

INTRODUCE

1. cat	car	cart	chat	chart	dart
2. far	jar	card	yard	smart	start
3. barn	bark	arm	art	part	park
4. scar	dark	large	star	hard	farm

5. Where can I park my car?

6. The farmer had a large, red barn.

REVIEW

7. snow	clean	please	music	try	she
8. float	might	wheat	breeze	speed	few

CHALLENGE

9. market marble marker target farmer smartest

Daily Practice

Directions: Do one activity each day. Then check the box.

☐ Build Fluency Read the words each day by yourself and to a partner.

☐ Mark It Circle all the words with ar.

☐ Spell It Have a partner say each word. Write the word. Check your answer.

☐ Write About It Use the words to create a story. Draw a box around the words from the list that you used.

Read-Spell-Write

Directions: Write each word two times. Say each letter as you write it.

1. work _____

2. again _____

3. eight _____

4. two _____

Use in Context

Directions: Complete each sentence with a word from above.
Read the finished sentences to a partner.

1. _____ people are on the farm.

2. Many bees in the hive _____ hard.

3. Carl rides in the cart _____.

4. The _____ dogs run in the park.

Connected Text

Directions: **Read the story. Then answer the questions.**

Art Day

It was Art Day in the park.
Kids made arts and crafts.

At two o'clock,
I made a jar out of clay.
I carved my name in large letters.

At six o'clock, I started again.
I made a scarf out of yarn.
It was dark blue.

By eight o'clock,
I had so much art!
Mom wheeled it home in a cart!

Interact with the Text

Directions: **Mark the text.**

1. Circle all the words with ar.

2. Draw a box around the word that rhymes with art.

Directions: **Write about the text.**

3. What did the kids make in the park? Tell a partner. Then write about it.

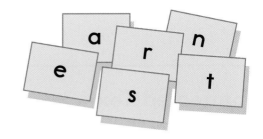

Sort It Out

**Directions: Read each word. Then sort the words.
Write each word in the correct box.**

| arm | art | bark | farm | harm |
| mark | park | shark | smart | start |

-arm

-art

-ark

What did you learn about how words work?

_____

_ _

_____

Think and Write

Directions: Listen to each picture name.
Write the spelling for each sound in a separate box.

1.

2.

3.

Listen and Spell

Directions: Write each word and sentence that you hear.

1. _____ **2.** _____

3. _____ **4.** _____

5. _____

Make New Words

Directions: Make words with the letter cards on page 446.
Write the words on the lines.

Name _____

On the Farm

Fold

1

Each day, Farmer Mark
works hard on his farm.

He starts in the barn.

He milks the cows.

He feeds the horse.

Fold

Farmer Mark sees stars in
the sky.

He drives home. It is time to
rest. Why?

The next day, Farmer Mark
will start his work again.

4

2

His two dogs are Red and Bud.

They bark and bark and bark.

Farmer Mark feeds them, too.

Then he feeds his hens.

He gets eggs from them.

The cornfield is far from the barn.

Farmer Mark drives his car.

He has a lot of help.

Eight men help him pick corn.

3

Transition to Longer Words

Directions: Choose a syllable from each box to make a word.
Then write the word.

car	gar	nap	pen	sand

cil	den	kin	pet	wich

1. _____ + _____ = _____

2. _____ + _____ = _____

3. _____ + _____ = _____

4. _____ + _____ = _____

5. _____ + _____ = _____

Directions: Complete the sentence with a word you wrote.

6. The _____ feels soft under my feet.

Read and Write

Directions: Say each picture name. Circle the word for the picture.
Write it on the line.

card yard yarn 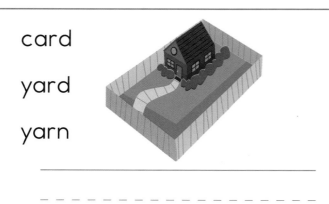 **1.** _____	scar star start **2.** _____
jar part tar **3.** _____	car cart far **4.** _____
bar bark barn  **5.** _____	shark tart yard **6.** _____

Build Fluency

Directions: Complete each sentence. Use at least one
word with ar.

1. They work _____.

2. I have more _____.

3. He could _____.

4. Two men _____.

Directions: Write a sentence using each word pair.

5. night, star

6. far, fly

Word Ladder

Directions: Listen to each clue. Then write the word.
Start at the bottom and climb to the top.

Something that is
not easy
Change one letter.

_____ _____ _____ _____

A big storm can
cause this.
Change one letter.

_____ _____ _____ _____

Animals are raised here.
Add one letter.

_____ _____ _____ _____

Not nearby
Change one letter.

_____ _____ _____

You ride in this on
the road.
Take away one letter.

_____ _____ _____

Start ➔ c a r t

Write About It

Directions: Read "On the Farm" again.
Write what you learned about Farmer Mark.

Fluency Check

Directions: Listen to the child read the word list. Mark one check in the green box if the word is read correctly (accuracy). Mark another check in the blue box if it is read automatically (fluency).

CUMULATIVE ASSESSMENT							
Lesson	**Word**			**Lesson**	**Word**		
20	bark	☐	☐	**17**	soap	☐	☐
	tar	☐	☐		slowly	☐	☐
	card	☐	☐		loaf	☐	☐
	farm	☐	☐		flown	☐	☐
19	few	☐	☐	**16**	bean	☐	☐
	cue	☐	☐		reading	☐	☐
	menu	☐	☐		seeds	☐	☐
	music	☐	☐		needed	☐	☐
18	try	☐	☐	**15**	brain	☐	☐
	might	☐	☐		gray	☐	☐
	brightest	☐	☐		sway	☐	☐
	flying	☐	☐		paintbrush	☐	☐

Number Correct (accuracy): _____ /24

Number Automatic (fluency): _____ /24

_____

_____

Learn and Blend

Directions: Listen and join in.

Ur as in her.
Ur as in bird.
Ur as in purple,
purse, and nurse.

> ### r-Controlled Vowels
> er   ir   ur

Blend It

Directions: Chorally read the words.

INTRODUCE

1.	hen	her	sit	sir	fist	first
2.	nurse	purse	curb	curl	burn	burst
3.	girl	turn	third	bird	stir	shirt
4.	hurt	serve	bath	birth	fan	fern

5. The girl got dirt on her green shirt.

6. Turn left at the third street you see.

REVIEW

7.	park	hard	few	night	bright	use
8.	float	slow	meat	deep	tray	drain

CHALLENGE

9. birthday firsthand party birdhouse return summer

Daily Practice

Directions: Do one activity each day. Then check the box.

☐ Build Fluency Read the words each day by yourself and to a partner.

☐ Mark It Circle all the words with ir. Underline all the words with ur.

☐ Spell It Have a partner say each word. Write the word. Check your answer.

☐ Write About It Use the words to create a story. Draw a box around the words from the list that you used.

Read-Spell-Write

Directions: Write each word two times. Say each letter as you write it.

1. your _____

2. because _____

3. always _____

4. want _____

Use in Context

Directions: Complete each sentence with a word from above.
Read the finished sentences to a partner.

1. Her bus is not _____ on time.

2. He left _____ he hurt his leg.

3. Do you _____ to be first in line?

4. There is a red bird in _____ yard.

Connected Text

Directions: **Read the how-to list. Then answer the questions.**

How to Make a Sandcastle

Want to make a sandcastle at the beach? Here's how.

- First, put sand in a pail. Add water, but not too much. That's because you want your wet sand to be firm.
- Second, stir your sand and water.
- Third, turn over the pail.
- Repeat these steps again and again. All that firm sand will turn into a big sandcastle.
- You can always find shells at the beach. Place some in a circle around your sandcastle.

Interact with the Text

Directions: **Mark the text.**

1. Circle all the words with ir.

2. Draw a box around the words with er.

Directions: **Write about the text.**

3. What do you stir in the pail? Tell a partner. Then write about it.

Word Sort

Sort It Out

Directions: Read each word. Then sort the words.
Write each word in the correct box.

bird	burn	dirt	first	girl
her	hurt	stir	turn	verb

er

ir

ur

What did you learn about how words work?

_____

- -

_____

Think and Write

Directions: Listen to each picture name. Write the spelling for each sound in a separate box.

1.

2.

3.

Listen and Spell

Directions: Write each word and sentence that you hear.

1. _____   2. _____

3. _____   4. _____

5. _____

Make New Words

Directions: Make words with the letter cards on page 446.
Write the words on the lines.

r-Controlled Vowels • Lesson 21

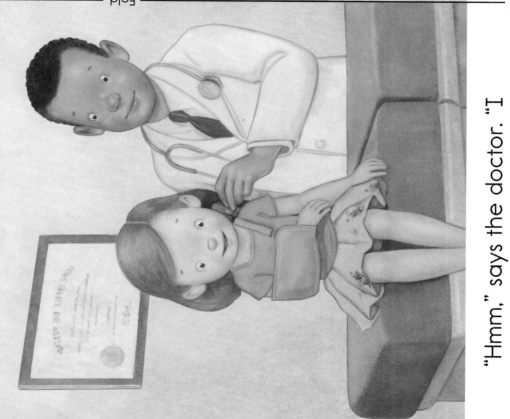

Name

Pam Gets Hurt

Fold

Fold

"Do you want to jump rope?" asks Fern.

"Can I go first?" asks Pam.

"You always go first," says Fern.

1

"Hmm," says the doctor. "I can fix your arm with a cast."

"But your skirt needs something different."

"Soap and water!"

4

2

Pam and Fern take turns.
Pam jumps faster and faster!
She trips and hurts her arm.
She gets dirt on her skirt.

Fold

Fold

Pam goes to the doctor.
"What did you do?" he asks.
"I hurt my arm," says Pam.
"And I got dirt on my skirt."

3

Transition to Longer Words

Directions: Choose a syllable from each box to make a word.
Then write the word.

bath	bird	far	sun	to

burn	day	house	mer	tub

1. _____ + _____ = _____

2. _____ + _____ = _____

3. _____ + _____ = _____

4. _____ + _____ = _____

5. _____ + _____ = _____

Directions: Write a sentence using a word you wrote.

6. _____

Read and Write

Directions: Say each picture name. Circle the word for the picture.
Write it on the line.

bird
dirt
fern

1. _____

curl
girl
turn

2. _____

first
nurse
purse

3. _____

fur
sir
stir

4. _____

bird
burn
purse

5. _____

shirt
skirt
surf

6. _____

Build Fluency

Directions: Complete each sentence. Use at least one word with er, ir, or ur.

1. I want _____.

2. We see eight _____.

3. They always _____.

4. Their friend _____.

Directions: Write a sentence using each word pair.

5. | card, her | _____ |

6. | dark, shade | _____ |

Word Ladder

Directions: Listen to each clue. Then write the word.
Start at the bottom and climb to the top.

An animal that flies and
has feathers

Take away two letters.
Add one letter.

_____ _____ _____ _____

Comes after first
and second

Take away two letters.
Add one letter.

_____ _____ _____ _____ _____

A feeling that you want
to drink something

Take away one letter.
Add two letters.

_____ _____ _____ _____ _____ _____

Comes before second
and third

Add two letters.

_____ _____ _____ _____ _____ _____

A tall evergreen tree

Change one letter.

_____ _____ _____

Start →   s   i   r

Write About It

Directions: Read "Pam Gets Hurt" again.
Write what you learned about Pam.

Fluency Check

Directions: Listen to the child read the word list. Mark one check in the green box if the word is read correctly (accuracy). Mark another check in the blue box if it is read automatically (fluency).

CUMULATIVE ASSESSMENT

Lesson	Word			Lesson	Word		
21	bird	☐	☐	18	try	☐	☐
	fern	☐	☐		might	☐	☐
	return	☐	☐		brightest	☐	☐
	girl	☐	☐		flying	☐	☐
20	bark	☐	☐	17	soap	☐	☐
	tar	☐	☐		slowly	☐	☐
	card	☐	☐		loaf	☐	☐
	farm	☐	☐		flown	☐	☐
19	few	☐	☐	16	bean	☐	☐
	cue	☐	☐		reading	☐	☐
	menu	☐	☐		seeds	☐	☐
	music	☐	☐		needed	☐	☐

Number Correct (accuracy): _____ /24

Number Automatic (fluency): _____ /24

Learn and Blend

Directions: Listen and join in.

Or as in store.
Or as in for.
Or as in oar, soar,
and roar.

r-Controlled Vowels

or   ore   oar

Blend It

Directions: Chorally read the words.

INTRODUCE

1. or	for	fork	oar	roar	soar
2. horn	corn	born	torn	sort	short
3. for	far	fur	more	tore	store
4. north	bored	sports	sore	shore	chores

5. Do you eat corn with a fork?

6. I tore my shirt on a thorn.

REVIEW

7. her	first	burn	purse	arm	bark
8. fight	dry	toast	blow	feet	team

CHALLENGE

9. forklift snowstorm shoreline northeast morning tornado

Daily Practice

Directions: Do one activity each day. Then check the box.

☐ **Build Fluency** Read the words each day by yourself and to a partner.

☐ **Mark It** Circle all the words with or. Underline all the words with oar.

☐ **Spell It** Have a partner say each word. Write the word. Check your answer.

☐ **Write About It** Use the words to create a story. Draw a box around the words from the list that you used.

Read-Spell-Write

Directions: Write each word two times. Say each letter as you write it.

1. open _____

_____

2. walk _____

_____

3. buy _____

_____

4. every _____

Use in Context

Directions: Complete each sentence with a word from above.
Read the finished sentences to a partner.

1. Help me _____ the can of corn.

2. I went to the shore _____ day.

3. We _____ more seed for the birds.

4. Will you _____ to the store?

Connected Text

Directions: **Read the story. Then answer the questions.**

Sports Fans

It's time for the game!
Open the gates.
Let the sports fans in.

First, they buy popcorn.
Then, they walk to their seats.
Look! Here comes the team.

Players run back and forth.
They jump! They dunk!
They score! The sports fans roar!

The horn blows. The game is over.
But the sports fans want more!

Interact with the Text

Directions: **Mark the text.**

1. Circle all the words with or and ore.

2. Draw a box around the words that rhyme with score.

Directions: **Write about the text.**

3. What do the sports fans want? Tell a partner. Then write about it.

Word Sort

Sort It Out

Directions: Read each word. Then sort the words.
Write each word in the correct box.

| corn | fork | more | oar | roar |
| score | short | soar | store | storm |

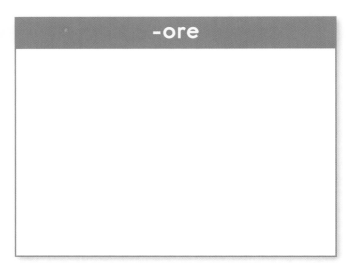

-or

-ore

-oar
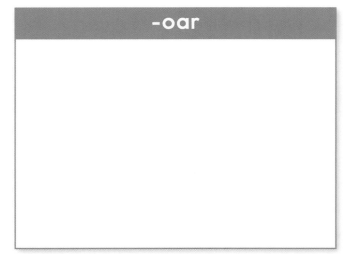

What did you learn about how words work?

_____

- -

_____

Think and Write

Directions: Listen to each picture name.
Write the spelling for each sound in a separate box.

1.

2.

3.

Listen and Spell

Directions: Write each word and sentence that you hear.

1. _____   **2.** _____

3. _____   **4.** _____

5. _____

Make New Words

Directions: Make words with the letter cards on page 446.
Write the words on the lines.

_____
- - - - - - - - - - - - - - - - -
_____

_____
- - - - - - - - - - - - - - - - -
_____

_____
- - - - - - - - - - - - - - - - -
_____

_____
- - - - - - - - - - - - - - - - -
_____

_____
- - - - - - - - - - - - - - - - -
_____

_____
- - - - - - - - - - - - - - - - -
_____

_____
- - - - - - - - - - - - - - - - -
_____

_____
- - - - - - - - - - - - - - - - -
_____

_____
- - - - - - - - - - - - - - - - -
_____

_____
- - - - - - - - - - - - - - - - -
_____

Name _____

Stores at the Mall

TOYS

BURGER SMOOTHIE PIZZA!

SALADS

We go to the mall.

We walk to the sports store.

Ben wants a ball.

Red or green?

1

Last we go to the food court.

We buy lunch and sit.

But not for long.

It's time to shop some more!

4

2

Next we walk to a clothing store.
We buy shorts, pants, and more!

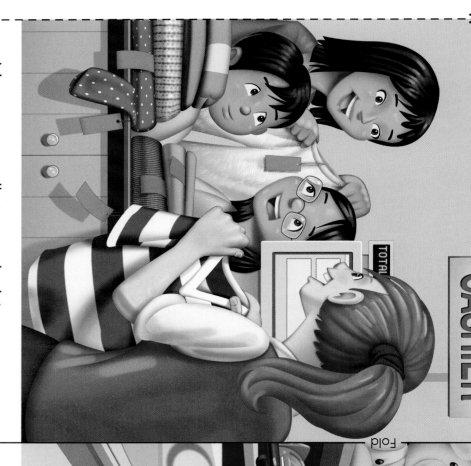

Fold

3

Then we walk to the toy store.
I buy a board game.
Ben wants every toy he sees.
Mom says, "No more, Ben!"

r-Controlled Vowels • Lesson 22

Prefixes (dis, pre)

Directions: Add **dis** to each word to make a new word. Then write the new word.

1. _____ like _____

2. _____ trust _____

Directions: Complete each sentence with a word you wrote.

3. I _____ people who are rude.

4. The cats _____ the sly fox.

Directions: Add **pre** to each word to make a new word. Then write the new word.

5. _____ heat _____

6. _____ plan _____

Directions: Complete each sentence with a word you wrote.

7. We _____ our trip to the farm.

8. _____ the oven first.

Read and Write

Directions: Say each picture name. Circle the word for the picture.
Write it on the line.

cork

corn

tore

1. _____

chore

horse

oars

2. _____

corn

form

horn

3. _____

fork

fort

roar

4. _____

porch

score

torch

5. _____

shore

shorts

soar

6. _____

Build Fluency

Directions: Complete each sentence. Use at least one word with or, ore, or oar.

1. I buy _____.

2. Together _____.

3. A different _____.

4. We walk to _____.

Directions: Write a sentence using each word pair.

5. | sports, tore | _____

_____

6. | first, fly | _____

_____

Word Ladder

Directions: Listen to each clue. Then write the word.
Start at the bottom and climb to the top.

This often brings wind and rain.
Change one letter.

_____ _____ _____ _____

You can buy eggs and milk here.
Change one letter.

_____ _____ _____ _____

A loud noise made by someone who is asleep
Change one letter.

_____ _____ _____ _____

You can find seashells here.
Add one letter.

_____ _____ _____ _____

A pitcher's arm might feel this way.
Change one letter.

_____ _____ _____ _____

Start ➞

m o r e

Write About It

Directions: Read "Stores at the Mall" again.
Write what you learned about shopping.

Fluency Check

Directions: Listen to the child read the word list. Mark one check in the green box if the word is read correctly (accuracy). Mark another check in the blue box if it is read automatically (fluency).

CUMULATIVE ASSESSMENT								
Lesson	Word			Lesson	Word			
22	form	☐	☐	**19**	few	☐	☐	
	shore	☐	☐		cue	☐	☐	
	board	☐	☐		menu	☐	☐	
	stored	☐	☐		music	☐	☐	
21	bird	☐	☐	**18**	try	☐	☐	
	fern	☐	☐		might	☐	☐	
	return	☐	☐		brightest	☐	☐	
	girl	☐	☐		flying	☐	☐	
20	bark	☐	☐	**17**	soap	☐	☐	
	tar	☐	☐		slowly	☐	☐	
	card	☐	☐		loaf	☐	☐	
	farm	☐	☐		flown	☐	☐	

Number Correct (accuracy): _____ /24

Number Automatic (fluency): _____ /24

Learn and Blend

Directions: Listen and join in.

Oo as in book.
Oo as in tune.
Oo as in blue, true,
and moon.

Short oo

oo

Long oo

oo	u_e	u
ew	ue	ou

Blend It

Directions: Chorally read the words.

INTRODUCE

1. hot	hoot	shot	shoot	lock	look
2. soon	spoon	moo	too	goose	loose
3. good	wood	book	cook	could	should
4. new	chew	flew	grew	glue	blue

5. We are in Room 3 at school.

6. I would like to read that book.

REVIEW

7. hurt	card	barn	art	dark	fork
8. short	roar	burn	more	smart	bird

CHALLENGE

9. toothbrush   bookshelf   schoolhouse   cookbook   bedroom

Daily Practice

Directions: Do one activity each day. Then check the box.

☐ Build Fluency Read the words each day by yourself and to a partner.

☐ Mark It Circle all the words with **oo**. Underline all the words with **ew**.

☐ Spell It Have a partner say each word. Write the word. Check your answer.

☐ Write About It Use the words to create a story. Draw a box around the words from the list that you used.

Read-Spell-Write

Directions: Write each word two times. Say each letter as you write it.

1. about

2. write

3. word

4. done

Use in Context

Directions: Complete each sentence with a word from above.
Read the finished sentences to a partner.

1. The new book is _____ a goose.

2. He has _____ a good job.

3. What is the _____ for this clue?

4. I would like to _____ a fun tune.

Connected Text

Directions: **Read the letter. Then answer the questions.**

Dear Grandma,

I wanted to write to you
about the trip we took.
We stayed at a cabin in the woods.
At night, we stood outside to look at the moon.

It was very cool.

One night, a raccoon ran past us.
Crash . . . Boom!
It took food from the trash.

We are going back in June.
Do you want to come, too?

Love,
Sue

Interact with the Text

Directions: **Mark the text.**

1. Circle all the words that rhyme with moon.

2. Draw a box around the words that rhyme with book.

Directions: **Write about the text.**

3. When is Sue going back to the cabin? Tell a partner. Then write about it.

Sort It Out

Directions: Read each word. Then sort the words.
Write each word in the correct box.

boot	brook	cook	goose	hoot
noon	shook	soon	stood	wood

oo (book)	oo (room)

What did you learn about how words work?

_____

- - - - - - - - - - - - - - - - - - - -

_____

Think and Write

Directions: Listen to each picture name. Write the spelling for each sound in a separate box.

1.

2.

3.

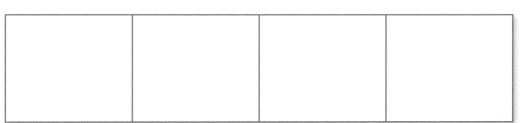

Listen and Spell

Directions: Write each word and sentence that you hear.

1. _____

2. _____

3. _____

4. _____

5. _____

Make New Words

Directions: Make words with the letter cards on page 446.
Write the words on the lines.

Short oo, Long oo • Lesson 23

Name _____

Books, Books, Books!

Authors write books.

Books are filled with words.

Books can be true. They can be made up, too.

Books can be funny or sad.

1

When you are done reading, you can choose a new book.

But don't forget one rule.

Take it back to the library when it's due!

4

2

Books tell about many things.
Like how to cook soup.
How to shoot hoops.
Or how to tune a flute.

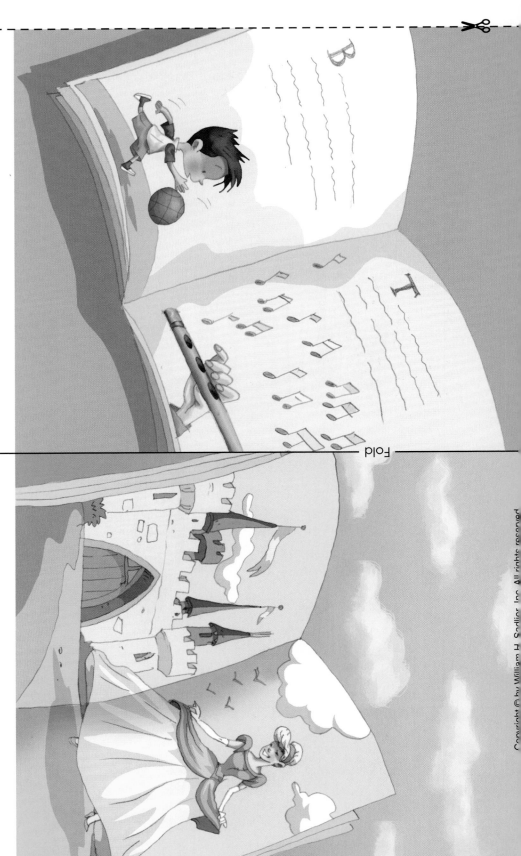

Fold

Fold

Books tell why the sky is blue.
And why sheep have wool.
Books can take you to new places.

3

_____

_____

Suffixes (ly, y)

Directions: Add ly to each word to make a new word.
Then write the new word.

1. quick _____ _____

2. safe _____ _____

3. sweet _____ _____

Directions: Add y to each word to make a new word.
Then write the new word.

4. dirt _____ _____

5. rain _____ _____

6. stick _____ _____

Directions: Complete each sentence with a word you wrote.

7. My hat fell in the _____ water.

8. A bird in the tree sang _____.

Read and Write

Directions: Say each picture name. Circle the word for the picture.
Write it on the line.

book
brook
cook

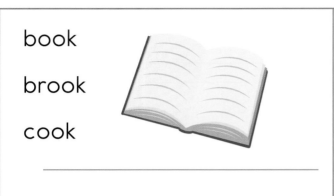

1. _____

moon
noon
room

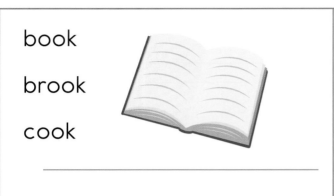

2. _____

boot
goose
roof

3. _____

blue
flute
glue

4. _____

foot
hood
hook

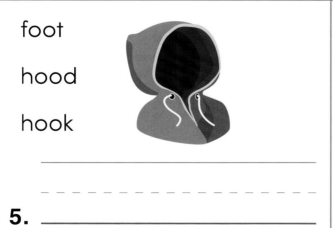

5. _____

brook
broom
roof

6. _____

Build Fluency

Directions: Complete each sentence. Use at least one word with oo.

1. Open your _____.

2. I want _____.

3. She would _____.

4. We always _____.

Directions: Write a sentence using each word pair.

5. room, turn _____

6. cook, corn _____

Directions: Listen to each clue. Then write the word. Start at the bottom and climb to the top.

A fast car can move this way.
Add one letter.

____ ____ ____ ____

You can visit all kinds of animals here.
Change one letter.

____ ____ ____

A ghost might say this in a scary story.
Take away one letter.

____ ____ ____

On snowy days, wear one on each foot.
Change one letter.

____ ____ ____ ____

An owl makes this sound at night.
Add one letter.

____ ____ ____ ____

Start →

h o t

Write About It

Directions: Read "Books, Books, Books!" again.
Write what you learned about books.

Fluency Check

Directions: Listen to the child read the word list. Mark one check in the green box if the word is read correctly (accuracy). Mark another check in the blue box if it is read automatically (fluency).

CUMULATIVE ASSESSMENT							
Lesson	Word			Lesson	Word		
23	stood	☐	☐	**20**	bark	☐	☐
	roots	☐	☐		tar	☐	☐
	glue	☐	☐		card	☐	☐
	looking	☐	☐		farm	☐	☐
22	form	☐	☐	**19**	few	☐	☐
	shore	☐	☐		cue	☐	☐
	board	☐	☐		menu	☐	☐
	stored	☐	☐		music	☐	☐
21	bird	☐	☐	**18**	try	☐	☐
	fern	☐	☐		might	☐	☐
	return	☐	☐		brightest	☐	☐
	girl	☐	☐		flying	☐	☐

Number Correct (accuracy): _____ /24

Number Automatic (fluency): _____ /24

Learn and Blend

Directions: Listen and join in.

Ow as in out.
Ow as in town, down,
and clown.

Diphthong /ou/

ou   ow

Blend It

Directions: Chorally read the words.

INTRODUCE

1. shot	shout	moth	mouth	fund	found
2. cow	now	down	town	brown	clown
3. round	sound	south	mouth	mouse	house
4. couch	ground	how	frown	about	growl

5. How do I drive to the next town?

6. My house is south of this town.

REVIEW

7. stir	verb	room	burn	group	serve
8. roar	porch	blue	took	park	fork

CHALLENGE

9. downtown   doghouse   dropout   somehow   thundercloud

Daily Practice

Directions: Do one activity each day. Then check the box.

☐ Build Fluency Read the words each day by yourself and to a partner.

☐ Mark It Circle all the words with ou. Underline all the words with ow.

☐ Spell It Have a partner say each word. Write the word. Check your answer.

☐ Write About It Use the words to create a story. Draw a box around the words from the list that you used.

Read-Spell-Write

Directions: Write each word two times. Say each letter as you write it.

1. after

2. pull

3. goes

4. laugh

Use in Context

Directions: Complete each sentence with a word from above.
Read the finished sentences to a partner.

1. The cat ran _____ the mouse.

2. Our car _____ down the road.

3. The clown made me _____.

4. How do the dogs _____ the sled?

Connected Text

Directions: **Read the poem. Then answer the questions.**

Flowers All Around

It is spring!
But when we look down,
the ground is so brown.

Mom goes to the store.
She buys seeds and much more.
We pull weeds from the ground
and drop seeds all around.

After days of showers,
the seeds sprout flowers!
Now the ground is not brown.
There are flowers all around!

Interact with the Text

Directions: **Mark the text.**

1. Circle all the words with ou.

2. Draw a box around the words with ow.

Directions: **Write about the text.**

3. What do the seeds sprout? Tell a partner. Then write about it.

Word Sort

Sort It Out

Directions: Read each word. Then sort the words.
Write each word in the correct box.

| brown | count | cow | down | found |
| house | how | loud | now | sound |

ou	**ow**

What did you learn about how words work?

_____

- -

_____

Think and Write

Directions: Listen to each picture name. Write the spelling for each sound in a separate box.

1.

2.

3.

Listen and Spell

Directions: Write each word and sentence that you hear.

1. _____

2. _____

3. _____

4. _____

5. _____

Make New Words

Directions: Make words with the letter cards on page 446.
Write the words on the lines.

Name _____

The Parade Is in Town!

Fold

Wow! There is a big crowd.

We can't be late.

The parade has started in our town.

1

After the parade, we walk back to our house.

Now I am sad. Oh, how I like a parade.

I hope it comes back soon!

4

2

A dad pulls a wagon.

The band plays.

A big round drum goes
boom-boom-boom.

It's such a loud sound.

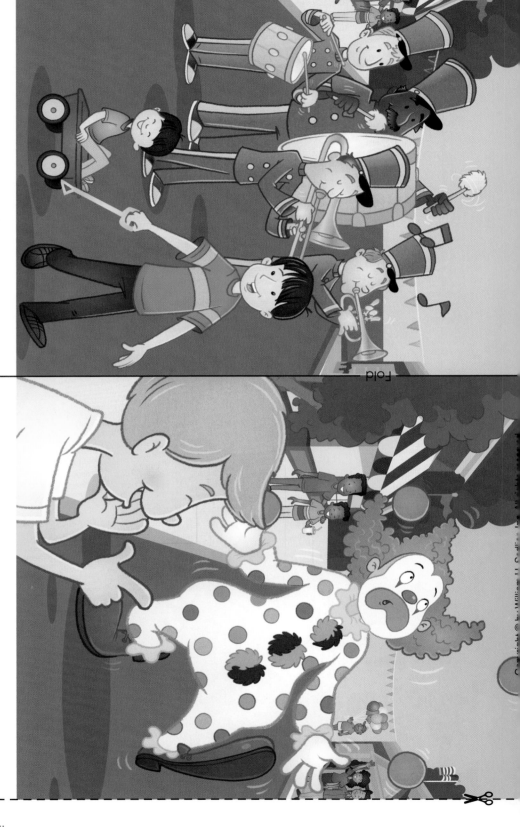

I laugh as a clown goes by.

He has big brown shoes.

His mouth turns down like a
frown.

His nose is red and round.

3

Word Study

Compound Words

Directions: Choose a word from each box to make a compound word.
Then write the compound word.

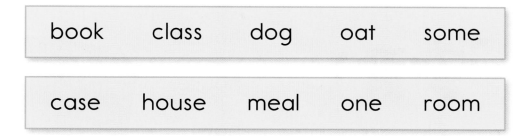

| book | class | dog | oat | some |

| case | house | meal | one | room |

1. _____ + _____ = _____

2. _____ + _____ = _____

3. _____ + _____ = _____

4. _____ + _____ = _____

5. _____ + _____ = _____

Directions: Complete the sentence with a word you wrote.

6. I ate a bowl of _____.

Read and Write

Directions: Say each picture name. Circle the word for the picture.
Write it on the line.

clown

cow

how

1. _____

hound

house

howl

2. _____

scout

shout

south

3. _____

cloud

clown

crown

4. _____

couch

mouse

mouth

5. _____

brown

found

frown

6. _____

Build Fluency

Directions: Complete each sentence. Use at least one word
with ou or ow.

1. She goes _____.

2. We laugh _____.

3. Every day _____.

4. They work _____.

Directions: Write a sentence using each word pair.

5. room, sound _____

6. horn, now _____

Word Ladder

Directions: Listen to each clue. Then write the word.
Start at the bottom and climb to the top.

You might see this
performer at a circus.
Change one letter.

_____ _____ _____ _____ _____

A king may wear this on
his head.
Change one letter.

_____ _____ _____ _____ _____

An acorn is this color.
Add one letter.

_____ _____ _____ _____ _____

The word "eye" plus this
word makes a
compound word.
Take away one letter.
Add two letters.

_____ _____ _____ _____

This animal makes a
"moo" sound.
Change one letter.

_____ _____ _____

Start ➡ n o w

Write About It

Directions: Read "The Parade Is in Town!" again.
Write what you learned about the parade.

Fluency Check

Directions: Listen to the child read the word list. Mark one check in the green box if the word is read correctly (accuracy). Mark another check in the blue box if it is read automatically (fluency).

Lesson	Word			Lesson	Word		
24	loud	☐	☐	**21**	bird	☐	☐
	frown	☐	☐		fern	☐	☐
	wow	☐	☐		return	☐	☐
	downtown	☐	☐		girl	☐	☐
23	stood	☐	☐	**20**	bark	☐	☐
	roots	☐	☐		tar	☐	☐
	glue	☐	☐		card	☐	☐
	looking	☐	☐		farm	☐	☐
22	form	☐	☐	**19**	few	☐	☐
	shore	☐	☐		cue	☐	☐
	board	☐	☐		menu	☐	☐
	stored	☐	☐		music	☐	☐

CUMULATIVE ASSESSMENT

Number Correct (accuracy): _____ /24

Number Automatic (fluency): _____ /24

Learn and Blend

Directions: Listen and join in.

Oy as in coin.
Oy as in toy, boy,
and joy.

Diphthong /oi/

oi   oy

Blend It

Directions: Chorally read the words.

INTRODUCE

1. boy   toy   joy   join   most   moist
2. oil   boil   broil   point   pointed   pointing
3. soil   spoil   coin   noise   voice   choice
4. sail   soil   seal   fail   foil   feel
5. The boy broke his best toy.
6. Roy lost his voice from yelling.

REVIEW

7. brown   food   clouds   good   tooth   could
8. blue   third   bird   purse   jar   short

CHALLENGE

9. enjoy   cowboy   boyfriend oily   noisy   joyful

Daily Practice

Directions: Do one activity each day. Then check the box.

☐ Build Fluency Read the words each day by yourself and to a partner.

☐ Mark It Circle all the words with **oi**. Underline all the words with **oy**.

☐ Spell It Have a partner say each word. Write the word. Check your answer.

☐ Write About It Use the words to create a story. Draw a box around the words from the list that you used.

Read-Spell-Write

Directions: Write each word two times. Say each letter as you write it.

1. four _____

2. any _____

3. better _____

4. only _____

Use in Context

Directions: Complete each sentence with a word from above.
Read the finished sentences to a partner.

1. The plant grows _____ in soil.

2. Did _____ new girls join the team?

3. The boy has _____ new toys.

4. I have _____ two coins left.

Connected Text

Directions: Read the how-to list. Then answer the questions.

How to Make a Royal Meal

You can make a meal fit for a king. Here's how!

- Only choose the best foods. The more food the better!
- You'll need to cook for at least four hours.
- Boil, bake, and broil. The food must be very hot.
- Put the food in foil. It will keep it moist. Do not let any spoil.
- Give the king choices. He likes seafood, such as oysters.
- Do your best work. Then the king may ask you to join him.

Enjoy!

Interact with the Text

Directions: Mark the text.

1. Circle all the words with oy.

2. Draw a box around the words that rhyme with soil.

Directions: Write about the text.

3. What does the king like to eat? Tell a partner. Then write about it.

Word Sort

Sort It Out

Directions: Read each word. Then sort the words. Write each word in the correct box.

| boil | boy | broil | coin | join |
| joy | noise | oil | soil | toy |

oi	oy

What did you learn about how words work?

_____

- -

_____

Think and Write

Directions: Listen to each picture name.
Write the spelling for each sound in a separate box.

1.

2.

3.

Listen and Spell

Directions: Write each word and sentence that you hear.

1. _____   2. _____

3. _____   4. _____

5. _____

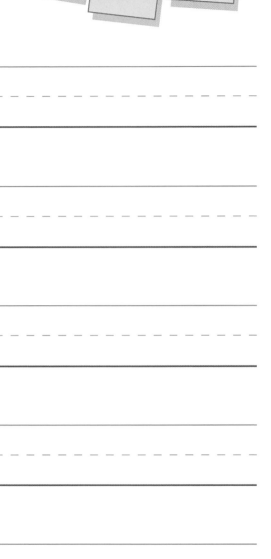

Make New Words

Directions: Make words with the letter cards on page 448.
Write the words on the lines.

Name _____

Join a Club!

Join a club and have fun with other boys and girls.

Pick any club you like.

There are many choices.

1

Fold

Troy joins the coin club.

He makes new friends.

What club would you like to join?

4

2

Joy joins the sports club.
Now she is better at soccer.
Make some noise for the sports club!

Roy joins the garden club.
He likes to dig in the soil.
Make some noise for the garden club!

3

Transition to Longer Words

Directions: Choose a syllable from each box to make a word.
Then write the word.

boil	down	joy	loud	muf

fin	ful	ing	ly	town

1. _____ + _____ = _____

2. _____ + _____ = _____

3. _____ + _____ = _____

4. _____ + _____ = _____

5. _____ + _____ = _____

Directions: Write a sentence using a word you wrote.

6. _____

Read and Write

Directions: Say each picture name. Circle the word for the picture.
Write it on the line.

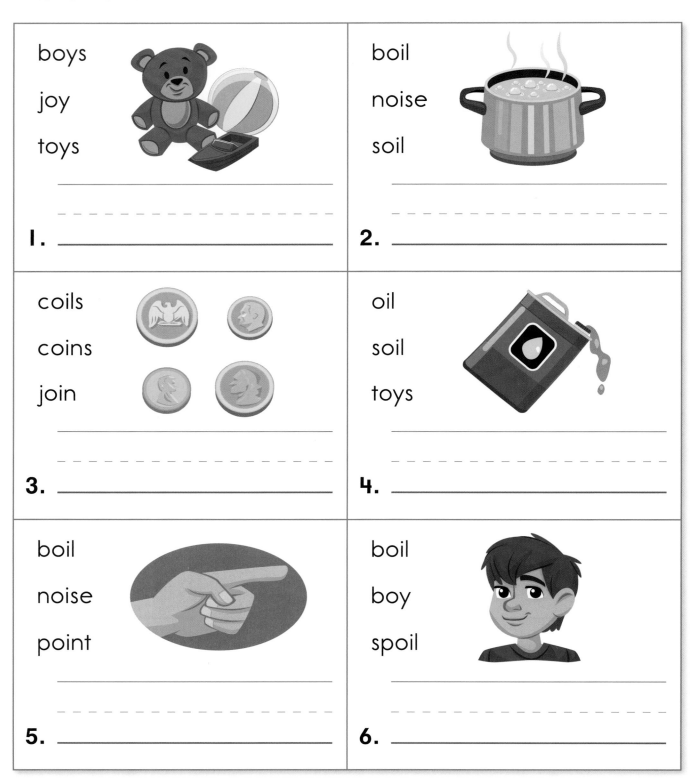

boys

joy

toys

1. _____

boil

noise

soil

2. _____

coils

coins

join

3. _____

oil

soil

toys

4. _____

boil

noise

point

5. _____

boil

boy

spoil

6. _____

Build Fluency

Directions: Complete each sentence. Use at least one word
with oi or oy.

1. Are any _____?

2. I need four _____.

3. After lunch _____.

4. Tell me about _____.

Directions: Write a sentence using each word pair.

boy, found

5. _____

room, soil

6. _____

Word Ladder

Directions: Listen to each clue. Then write the word.
Start at the bottom and climb to the top.

Do this to become a member of a club.

Change one letter.

_____ _____ _____ _____

This can be used to pay for something.

Change one letter.

_____ _____ _____ _____

A snake wraps its body in this ring shape.

Change one letter.

_____ _____ _____ _____

This is dirt that plants grow in.

Change one letter.

_____ _____ _____ _____

You do this to water when you heat it until it bubbles.

Add one letter.

_____ _____ _____ _____

Start ➔

o   i   l

Write About It

Directions: Read "Join a Club!" again.
Write what you learned about different kinds of clubs.

Fluency Check

Directions: Listen to the child read the word list. Mark one check in the green box if the word is read correctly (accuracy). Mark another check in the blue box if it is read automatically (fluency).

CUMULATIVE ASSESSMENT

Lesson	Word			Lesson	Word		
25	toys	☐	☐	**22**	form	☐	☐
	broil	☐	☐		shore	☐	☐
	coin	☐	☐		board	☐	☐
	enjoy	☐	☐		stored	☐	☐
24	loud	☐	☐	**21**	bird	☐	☐
	frown	☐	☐		fern	☐	☐
	wow	☐	☐		return	☐	☐
	downtown	☐	☐		girl	☐	☐
23	stood	☐	☐	**20**	bark	☐	☐
	roots	☐	☐		tar	☐	☐
	glue	☐	☐		card	☐	☐
	looking	☐	☐		farm	☐	☐

Number Correct (accuracy): _____ /24

Number Automatic (fluency): _____ /24

Learn and Blend

Directions: Listen and join in.

Aw as in yawn.
Aw as in fault.
Aw as in ball,
walk, and salt.

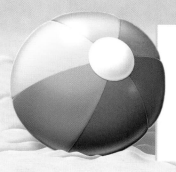

Complex Vowel /ô/		
au	aw	a(lk)
a(lt)	a(ll)	

Blend It

Directions: Chorally read the words.

INTRODUCE

1. saw	raw	law	paws	cause	because
2. all	ball	small	salt	talk	walk
3. tell	tall	lean	lawn	felt	fault
4. yawn	sauce	crawl	draw	call	chalk

5. The big bugs crawl up the wall!

6. Dawn likes to draw her house.

REVIEW

7. moon	sound	clown	took	shirt	glue
8. her	burn	spoon	mouth	storm	fork

CHALLENGE

9. drawing   ballplayer   dinosaur   always   lawnmower

Daily Practice

Directions: Do one activity each day. Then check the box.

☐ **Build Fluency** Read the words each day by yourself and to a partner.

☐ **Mark It** Circle all the words with au. Underline all the words with aw.

☐ **Spell It** Have a partner say each word. Write the word. Check your answer.

☐ **Write About It** Use the words to create a story. Draw a box around the words from the list that you used.

Read-Spell-Write

Directions: Write each word two times. Say each letter as you write it.

1. been _____

2. before _____

3. pretty _____

4. warm _____

Use in Context

Directions: Complete each sentence with a word from above.
Read the finished sentences to a partner.

1. I saw a _____ rose in the garden.

2. We go for a walk _____ lunch.

3. I put on shorts because it's _____.

4. Paul has _____ to the small park.

Connected Text

Directions: **Read the story. Then answer the questions.**

What Is It?

1. Leaves are on the lawn.
Days are not as warm.
It comes before winter.
What is it? (answer: autumn)

2. You can shop here.
For big things. Small things.
You can get a ball.
What is this place? (answer: a mall)

3. You can use it to draw on the sidewalk
or write on a blackboard.
What is it? (answer: chalk)

Interact with the Text

Directions: **Mark the text.**

1. Circle all the words with aw.

2. Draw a box around the words that rhyme with haul.

Directions: **Write about the text.**

3. What comes before winter? Tell a partner. Then write about it.

_____

- -

Word Sort

Sort It Out

Directions: **Read each word. Then sort the words.
Write each word in the correct box.**

ball	call	chalk	fall	halt
salt	small	talk	tall	walk

-all

-alt

-alk

What did you learn about how words work?

_____

- -

_____

370 **Complex Vowels** • Lesson 26

Think and Write

Directions: Listen to each picture name.
Write the spelling for each sound in a separate box.

1.

2.

3.

Listen and Spell

Directions: Write each word and sentence that you hear.

1. _____ 2. _____

3. _____ 4. _____

5. _____

Make New Words

Directions: Make words with the letter cards on page 448.
Write the words on the lines.

Complex Vowels • Lesson 26

Name _____

A Walk in the Park

Fold

Grandma and I took a walk in the park.

It was a warm day. Here's what we saw.

A dad taught his son to walk.

1

Fold

I wanted to draw all the things we saw in the park.

When we got home, that's just what I did!

4

2

We saw a pretty deer and her fawn. We saw a hawk, too. Then I saw a dog's paw marks on the path.

Fold

We saw people on the lawn. A girl waved at me. "Come play with us," she called. I ran and caught the ball. It was fun.

3

Inflectional Endings

Directions: Add s, ed, and ing to each word in the box to make new words. Write the new words on the lines. You may need to cross out the final e in a word before you add an ending.

hope	pick	save	show

1. _____

2. _____

3. _____

4. _____

Directions: Write a sentence using one of the words you wrote.

5. _____

Read and Write

Directions: Say each picture name. Circle the word for the picture.
Write it on the line.

chalk

fault

talk

1. _____

dawn

straw

yawn

2. _____

ball

call

tall

3. _____

law

saw

small

4. _____

hall

hawk

walk

5. _____

claw

crawl

lawn

6. _____

Build Fluency

Directions: Complete each sentence. Use at least one word
with au, aw, alk, alt, or all.

1. Before school _____.

2. Use only _____.

3. Warm up _____.

4. She goes _____.

Directions: Write a sentence using each word pair.

5. group, small _____

6. draw, round _____

Word Ladder

Directions: Listen to each clue. Then write the word.
Start at the bottom and climb to the top.

You do this when you say sentences.

Change one letter.

_____ _____ _____ _____

A baby can crawl but can't do this.

Change one letter.

_____ _____ _____ _____

You can hang a picture on this.

Change one letter.

_____ _____ _____ _____

A giraffe can reach high trees because it is this.

Change one letter.

_____ _____ _____ _____

A seal can balance this on its nose.

Change one letter.

_____ _____ _____ _____

Start → c a l l

Write About It

Directions: Read "A Walk in the Park" again.
Write what you learned about the walk in the park.

Fluency Check

Directions: Listen to the child read the word list. Mark one check in the green box if the word is read correctly (accuracy). Mark another check in the blue box if it is read automatically (fluency).

Lesson	Word			Lesson	Word		
26	dawn	☐	☐	23	stood	☐	☐
	talking	☐	☐		roots	☐	☐
	salt	☐	☐		glue	☐	☐
	hallway	☐	☐		looking	☐	☐
25	toys	☐	☐	22	form	☐	☐
	broil	☐	☐		shore	☐	☐
	coin	☐	☐		board	☐	☐
	enjoy	☐	☐		stored	☐	☐
24	loud	☐	☐	21	bird	☐	☐
	frown	☐	☐		fern	☐	☐
	wow	☐	☐		return	☐	☐
	downtown	☐	☐		girl	☐	☐

CUMULATIVE ASSESSMENT

Number Correct (accuracy): _____ /24

Number Automatic (fluency): _____ /24

Learn and Blend

Directions: Listen and join in.

Air as in share.
Air as in pair.
Air as in wear, tear,
and bear.

r-Controlled Vowels

are   air   ear

Blend It

Directions: Chorally read the words.

INTRODUCE

1. air	fair	hair	pair	chair	
2. care	dare	rare	share	square	
3. bear	wear	pear	scar	scare	

4. My hair is a big mess!

5. Please sit in your chair.

REVIEW

6. talk	boy	small	spoil	hawk	noise
7. ground	crown	salt	spoon	would	new

CHALLENGE

8. share   shared   sharing   care   careless   careful

Daily Practice

Directions: Do one activity each day. Then check the box.

☐ Build Fluency Read the words each day by yourself and to a partner.

☐ Mark It Circle all the words with **are**. Underline all the words with **air**.

☐ Spell It Have a partner say each word. Write the word. Check your answer.

☐ Write About It Use the words to create a story. Draw a box around the words from the list that you used.

Read-Spell-Write

Directions: Write each word two times. Say each letter as you write it.

1. once _____

2. upon _____

3. yellow _____

4. live _____

Use in Context

Directions: Complete each sentence with a word from above. Read the finished sentences to a partner.

1. _____ we took care of a hamster.

2. I placed the pear _____ the table.

3. Does the bear _____ in the woods?

4. I wear my _____ socks.

Connected Text

Directions: **Read the story. Then answer the questions.**

Fran and Jan

Fran and Jan are twins.
But they do not like to share.

They will not share a toy bear.
They will not share a big chair.
They will not share a doll with long yellow hair.
They will not share the things they wear.

Fran and Jan fight over all these things.
Mom and Dad try to teach the pair to be fair.
So after they fight, Fran and Jan make up.
Once they do, they share a hug.

Interact with the Text

Directions: **Mark the text.**

1. Circle all the words with air.

2. Draw a box around the words that rhyme with share.

Directions: **Write about the text.**

3. What do Fran and Jan share? Tell a partner. Then write about it.

Word Sort

Sort It Out

Directions: **Read each word. Then sort the words. Write each word in the correct box.**

bear	care	chair	dare	fair
hair	pair	pear	stare	wear

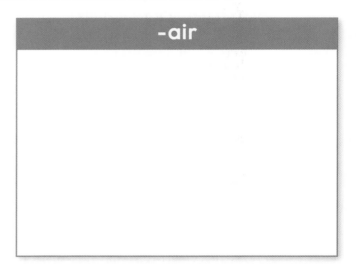

-are

-air

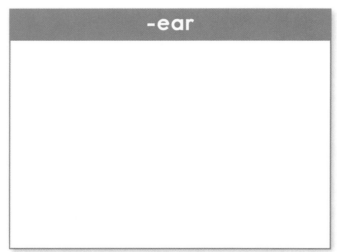

-ear

What did you learn about how words work?

_____

_____

Think and Write

Directions: Listen to each picture name.
Write the picture name on the line.

1.

_____

2.

_____

3.

_____

Listen and Spell

Directions: Write each word and sentence that you hear.

1. _____ **2.** _____

3. _____ **4.** _____

5. _____

Make New Words

Directions: Make words with the letter cards on page 448.
Write the words on the lines.

_____

- - - - - - - - - - - - - - - - -

_____

_____

- - - - - - - - - - - - - - - - -

_____

_____

- - - - - - - - - - - - - - - - -

_____

_____

- - - - - - - - - - - - - - - - -

_____

_____

- - - - - - - - - - - - - - - - -

_____

_____

- - - - - - - - - - - - - - - - -

_____

_____

- - - - - - - - - - - - - - - - -

_____

Name _____

The Three Bears: A Retelling

Fold

Once upon a time, there lived three bears.

These bears liked pears.

One day the bears went out.

1

"A girl is in my chair!"

"And she ate all of our pears!" yelled Little Bear.

"Don't you want to share?" asked the girl.

4

2

A girl with yellow hair went
into the bears' house.
She saw three pears.
One by one she ate each pear.

Soon the bears came home.
"Who ate my pear?" asked
Mom Bear and Dad Bear.
"Who ate my pear?" asked
Little Bear.

3

Transition to Longer Words

Directions: Choose a syllable from each box to make a word. Then write the word.

care	cloud	num	sun	wear

ber	ing	less	set	y

1. _____ + _____ = _____

2. _____ + _____ = _____

3. _____ + _____ = _____

4. _____ + _____ = _____

5. _____ + _____ = _____

Directions: Write a sentence using a word you wrote.

6. _____

Read and Write

Directions: Say each picture name. Circle the word for the picture.
Write it on the line.

scare

skate

skirt

1. _____

star

stare

stir

2. _____

barn

bear

bird

3. _____

scar

share

square

4. _____

Directions: Circle the two words that rhyme with share. Write the words on the lines.

| first | pair | wear | work |

5. _____   6. _____

Build Fluency

Directions: Complete each sentence. Use at least one word with are, air, or ear.

1. The yellow _____.

2. Do not pull _____.

3. Four bears _____.

4. Once I _____.

Directions: Write a sentence using each word pair.

5. | look, wear | _____ |

6. | mouse, scare | _____ |

Word Ladder

Directions: Listen to each clue. Then write the word.
Start at the bottom and climb to the top.

What you sit on
Add one letter.

_____ _____ _____ _____ _____

A bald person doesn't
have any.
Change one letter.

_____ _____ _____ _____

A fun place where you
go on rides and win
prizes
Add one letter.

_____ _____ _____ _____ _____

Not near
Take away one letter.

_____ _____ _____

What you pay to ride on
a train
Change one letter.

_____ _____ _____ _____

Start ➡ c a r e

Write About It

Directions: Read "The Three Bears: A Retelling" again.
Write what you learned about the bears.

Cumulative
Assessment

Fluency Check

Directions: Listen to the child read the word list. Mark one check in the green box if the word is read correctly (accuracy). Mark another check in the blue box if it is read automatically (fluency).

Lesson	Word			Lesson	Word		
27	care	☐	☐	**24**	loud	☐	☐
	upstairs	☐	☐		frown	☐	☐
	share	☐	☐		wow	☐	☐
	bear	☐	☐		downtown	☐	☐
26	dawn	☐	☐	**23**	stood	☐	☐
	talking	☐	☐		roots	☐	☐
	salt	☐	☐		glue	☐	☐
	hallway	☐	☐		looking	☐	☐
25	toys	☐	☐	**22**	form	☐	☐
	broil	☐	☐		shore	☐	☐
	coin	☐	☐		board	☐	☐
	enjoy	☐	☐		stored	☐	☐

CUMULATIVE ASSESSMENT

Number Correct (accuracy): _____ /24

Number Automatic (fluency): _____ /24

Copyright © by William H. Sadlier, Inc. All rights reserved.

r-Controlled Vowels • Lesson 27

UNIT 6

Dear Family,

In this unit, your child will learn about words that contain more long vowel spellings. He or she will learn to read words with long **i** (ild, ind, ie,), such as **wild**; **kind**; **pie**; and long **o** (old, oe), such as **sold**; **toes**; and long **e** (y, ey, ie), such as **happy**; **money**; and **chief**.

Read Connected Text

For each week's lesson, your child will read a Take-Home Book that focuses on the lesson skill. At week's end, the book will be sent home with your child. Read the book to your child, or read it aloud together, pointing to each word as you say it. Multiple readings of each Take-Home Book will give your child practice with the lesson skills.

Practice with the Take-Home Book

After reading, go back through the book and ask your child to point to words in the story that include the long vowel spellings for that lesson.

Have your child tell you about the book in one sentence. Write what your child says and read the description aloud together.

Lesson Skills and Take-Home Books

Lesson 28: Long **i** (**ild, ind**) and long **o** (**old**): "Kind Child, Wild Child"
Lesson 29: Long **i** (**ie**) and long **o** (**oe**) "Moe's Diner"
Lesson 30: Long **e** (**y, ey, ie**) "A Super Silly Story"

Extend the Learning

With your child, look for words with more long vowel spellings in books, signs, magazine covers, etc. Keep a notebook of words you discover.

Challenge your child to identify objects in your home or other locations that have more long vowel spellings. For example, "I spy a pie."

Visit SadlierConnect.com for Student & Family Resources.

Apreciada familia:

En esta unidad, su niño(a) aprenderá acerca de palabras con vocales con sonidos más largos. Aprenderá a leer palabras con el sonido largo de la **i** (ild, ind, ie), como **wild**; **kind**; **pie**; de la **o** larga (old, oe), como **sold**; **toes**; y de la **e** larga (y, ey, ie), como **happy**; **money** y **chief**.

Leyendo la historieta en el Take-Home Book

Para cada lección de la semana su niño(a) leerá un cuadernillo de historietas, Take-Home Book, que se enfoca en las destrezas de la lección. Al final de cada semana su niño(a) llevará el cuadernillo a la casa. Lea la historieta a su niño(a) o leánla en voz alta juntos, señalando cada palabra al decirla. Leer varias veces ayudará a su niño(a) a practicar las destrezas de la lección.

Practicando con el Take-Home Book

Pida a su niño(a) señalar palabras en la historieta con vocales con sonido más largo para esa lección. Luego pídale que resuma la historieta en una frase. Escriba lo que dice su niño(a) y lean juntos lo que escribió.

Lesson Skills and Take-Home Books

Lesson 28 Long **i** (**ild**, **ind**) and long **o** (**old**): "Kind Child, Wild Child"
Lesson 29 Long **i** (**ie**) and long **o** (**oe**): "Moe's Diner"
Lesson 30 Long **e** (**y**, **ey**, **ie**): "My Super Silly Story"

Ampliando el aprendizaje

Con su niño(a) busque palabras con vocales con sonido más largo en libros, letreros, portadas de revistas, etc. Haga una libreta con palabras que descubran juntos.

Rete a su niño(a) a identificar, ya sea en su casa o en otros lugares, objetos con vocales con sonido más largo. Por ejemplo: "I spy a pie."

 Visite SadlierConnect.com **para recursos para el estudiante y la familia.**

Learn and Blend

Directions: Listen and join in.

I as in child and find.
O as in cold, sold,
and gold.

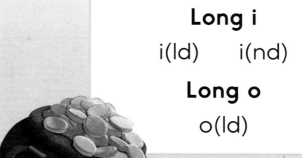

Long i
i(ld)   i(nd)
Long o
o(ld)

Blend It

Directions: Chorally read the words.

INTRODUCE

1. will	wild	chill	child	kid	kind
2. find	mind	old	cold	sold	told
3. fold	mile	mild	blind	hold	hole

4. That child is very kind.

5. It is so cold when it snows!

REVIEW

6. bear	walking	share	salt	stairs	sauce
7. straw	claws	toys	boil	sound	mouse

CHALLENGE

8. child	children	kind	kindness	old	oldest

Daily Practice

Directions: Do one activity each day. Then check the box.

☐ Build Fluency Read the words each day by yourself and to a partner.

☐ Mark It Circle all the words with **ild**. Underline all the words with **ind**.

☐ Spell It Have a partner say each word. Write the word. Check your answer.

☐ Write About It Use the words to create a story. Draw a box around the words from the list that you used.

Read-Spell-Write

Directions: Write each word two times. Say each letter as you write it.

1. even

2. never

3. most

4. another

Use in Context

Directions: Complete each sentence with a word from above.
Read the finished sentences to a partner.

1. Did a child catch the _____ fish?

2. He doesn't _____ mind the cold!

3. The man _____ sold his house.

4. I plant _____ kind of flower.

Connected Text

Directions: **Read the story. Then answer the questions.**

A Good Pet

There are all kinds of dogs.
You will find that most make good pets.
A dog can live with another dog,
a small child, or even a cat in a house!

Teach your dog to mind you.
Say "Sit," or "Come."
Soon you'll find your dog does what he's told.

Never let your dog run wild.
Never leave your dog out in the cold.
Be kind to your dog.

Your dog will always be your friend!

Interact with the Text

Directions: **Mark the text.**

1. Circle all the words with long i.

2. Draw a box around the words that rhyme with hold.

Directions: **Write about the text.**

3. Is a dog a good pet? Tell a partner. Then write about it.

Word Sort

Sort It Out

Directions: Read each word. Then sort the words.
Write each word in the correct box.

blind	child	cold	find	fold
kind	mild	told	sold	wild

-ild

-ind

-old

What did you learn about how words work?

_____

- - - - - - - - - - - - - - - - - -

_____

Long i, Long o • Lesson 28

Think and Write

Directions: Listen to each picture name.
Write the spelling for each sound in a separate box.

1.

2.

3.

Listen and Spell

Directions: Write each word and sentence that you hear.

1. _____

2. _____

3. _____

4. _____

5. _____

Make New Words

Directions: Make words with the letter cards on page 448.
Write the words on the lines.

Name

Kind Child, Wild Child

Fold

Fold

The wild child will not eat his dinner.

He only wants cold cheese.

The kind child eats most of his meal, even his peas!

The wild child never helps.

He says, "I don't care."

The kind child helps Dad.

He looks both here and there.

4

2

The wild child eats lots
of treats.

He doesn't do as he's told.

The kind child has just one.

To ask for another is bold.

The wild child never helps.

He tends to make a mess.

The kind child helps Mom
fold things.

He likes to do his best.

3

Transition to Longer Words

Directions: Choose a syllable from each box to make a word.
Then write the word.

act	bub	find	kind	old

ble	ed	est	ing	ly

1. _____ + _____ = _____

2. _____ + _____ = _____

3. _____ + _____ = _____

4. _____ + _____ = _____

5. _____ + _____ = _____

Directions: Write a sentence using a word you wrote.

6. _____

Read and Write

Directions: Say each picture name. Circle the word for the picture.
Write it on the line.

bold cold told		child hive kind	

1. _____

2. _____

find fold sold		mild mind smile	

3. _____

4. _____

close globe scold		bold gold hole	

5. _____

6. _____

Build Fluency

Directions: Complete each sentence. Use at least one word
with ild, ind, or old.

1. We never _____.

2. Most people _____.

3. It has been _____.

4. We live _____.

Directions: Write a sentence using each word pair.

5. | ball, find | _____

6. | child, found | _____

Word Ladder

Directions: Listen to each clue. Then write the word.
Start at the bottom and climb to the top.

It is the past tense
of "tell."
Change one letter.

Do this with a towel
before putting it away.
Change one letter.

A word that means you
like someone
Change one letter.

When something is lost
you try to do this.
Change one letter.

You can do this with
some clocks.
Change one letter.

Start ➞ w   i   l   d

Write About It

Directions: Read "Kind Child, Wild Child" again. Write what you learned about the kind child and the wild child.

Fluency Check

Directions: Listen to the child read the word list. Mark one check in the green box if the word is read correctly (accuracy). Mark another check in the blue box if it is read automatically (fluency).

CUMULATIVE ASSESSMENT							
Lesson	Word			Lesson	Word		
28	child	☐	☐	25	toys	☐	☐
	kind	☐	☐		broil	☐	☐
	sold	☐	☐		coin	☐	☐
	golden	☐	☐		enjoy	☐	☐
27	care	☐	☐	24	loud	☐	☐
	upstairs	☐	☐		frown	☐	☐
	share	☐	☐		wow	☐	☐
	bear	☐	☐		downtown	☐	☐
26	dawn	☐	☐	23	stood	☐	☐
	talking	☐	☐		roots	☐	☐
	salt	☐	☐		glue	☐	☐
	hallway	☐	☐		looking	☐	☐

Number Correct (accuracy): _____ /24

Number Automatic (fluency): _____ /24

Learn and Blend

Directions: Listen and join in.

I as in cries.
O as in toes.
And that's how the story goes.

Long i
ie
Long o
oe

Blend It

Directions: Chorally read the words.

INTRODUCE

1.	pie	tie	die	dried	cried	tried
2.	flies	skies	dries	tries	pies	lies
3.	toe	toes	Joe	Joe's	goes	go

4. I could eat a whole pie!

5. Do you eat a lot of fried food?

REVIEW

6.	child	kind	cold	sold	wear	stare
7.	chairs	small	chalk	draw	joy	noise

CHALLENGE

8.	toe	tiptoe	tie	necktie	fried	friend

Daily Practice

Directions: Do one activity each day. Then check the box.

☐ Build Fluency Read the words each day by yourself and to a partner.

☐ Mark It Circle all the words with **ie**. Underline all the words with **oe**.

☐ Spell It Have a partner say each word. Write the word. Check your answer.

☐ Write About It Use the words to create a story. Draw a box around the words from the list that you used.

Read-Spell-Write

Directions: Write each word two times. Say each letter as you write it.

1. number _____

2. today _____

3. special _____

4. over _____

Use in Context

Directions: Complete each sentence with a word from above. Read the finished sentences to a partner.

1. We made a _____ pie for him.

2. The hawk flies _____ the trees.

3. The _____ is less than five.

4. I put my toes in the water _____.

Connected Text

Directions: **Read the story. Then answer the questions.**

What Is It?

1. I wear it on special days. Like today!
It goes around my neck.
I try to put it on myself.
But that's hard to do.
What is it?   (answer: tie)

2. It goes up when rain comes down.
What is it?   (answer: umbrella)

3. You can use them in a number of ways.
Sometimes I use them in a cake or a pie.
But I like to eat them fried.
What are they?   (answer: eggs)

Interact with the Text

Directions: **Mark the text.**

1. Circle all the words with ie.

2. Draw a box around the words that rhyme with toes.

Directions: **Write about the text.**

3. What does the child eat that is fried? Tell a partner. Then write about it.

_____

- -

_____

Word Sort

Sort It Out

Directions: Read each word. Then sort the words.
Write each word in the correct box.

| cried | die | doe | dried | goes |
| Joe | pie | tie | toe | tried |

ie	oe

What did you learn about how words work?

_____

- -

_____

Think and Write

Directions: Listen to each picture name.
Write the spelling for each sound in a separate box.

1.

2.

3.

Listen and Spell

Directions: Write each word and sentence that you hear.

1. _____

2. _____

3. _____

4. _____

5. _____

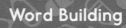

Make New Words

Directions: Make words with the letter cards on page 448.
Write the words on the lines.

_____

- -

_____

_____

- -

_____

_____

- -

_____

_____

- -

_____

_____

- -

_____

Moe's Diner

Name _____

"Today's special is pies,"
says Moe.

Joe looks at the menu.

"I will try Pie Number Nine,"
he says.

1

Joe runs out of Moe's Diner.

He goes to Poe's Diner.

"Today's special is cheese,"
says Poe.

Joe smiles. "That is fine!"

4

2

Joe digs in, but a bluebird flies out!

"What is this?" cries Joe.

"It's Bluebird Pie," says Moe.

"No, no, no!" says Joe.

Moe brings Joe a new pie.

"This is my best pie!" says Moe. "Pie Number Five."

Joe tries it. A redbird flies out!

3

Transition to Longer Words

Directions: Choose a syllable from each box to make a word. Then write the word.

box	kit	sneak	toe	with

es	ing	nail	out	ten

1. _____ + _____ = _____

2. _____ + _____ = _____

3. _____ + _____ = _____

4. _____ + _____ = _____

5. _____ + _____ = _____

Directions: Write a sentence using a word you wrote.

6. _____

Read and Write

Directions: Say each picture name. Circle the word for the picture.
Write it on the line.

die
pie
dry

1. _____

lie
tie
try

2. _____

die
doe
toe

3. _____

boat
bow
toad

4. _____

float
flow
glow

5. _____

blow
bow
cloak

6. _____

Build Fluency

Directions: Complete each sentence. Use at least one word
with ie or oe.

1. Today she _____.

2. Over there _____.

3. I never _____.

4. They live _____.

Directions: Write a sentence using each word pair.

5. | flies, old | _____

6. | chair, goes | _____

Word Ladder

Directions: Listen to each clue. Then write the word.
Start at the bottom and climb to the top.

You have five of these
on each foot.

Add one letter.

_____ _____ _____ _____

This is part of your foot.

Change one letter.

_____ _____ _____

A man might wear this
around his neck.

Take away one letter.

_____ _____ _____

What Mom did with the
laces on her shoes

Take away two letters.
Add one letter.

_____ _____ _____ _____ _____

What the boy did when
he hurt his foot

Change one letter.

_____ _____ _____ _____

Start → f r i e d

Write About It

Directions: Read "Moe's Diner" again.
Write what you learned about Joe.

Fluency Check

Directions: Listen to the child read the word list. Mark one check in the green box if the word is read correctly (accuracy). Mark another check in the blue box if it is read automatically (fluency).

CUMULATIVE ASSESSMENT					
Lesson	Word			Lesson	Word		
29	pie	☐ ☐	26	dawn	☐ ☐
	fried	☐ ☐		talking	☐ ☐
	goes	☐ ☐		salt	☐ ☐
	tiptoe	☐ ☐		hallway	☐ ☐
28	child	☐ ☐	25	toys	☐ ☐
	kind	☐ ☐		broil	☐ ☐
	sold	☐ ☐		coin	☐ ☐
	golden	☐ ☐		enjoy	☐ ☐
27	care	☐ ☐	24	loud	☐ ☐
	upstairs	☐ ☐		frown	☐ ☐
	share	☐ ☐		wow	☐ ☐
	bear	☐ ☐		downtown	☐ ☐

Number Correct (accuracy): _____ /24

Number Automatic (fluency): _____ /24

Learn and Blend

Directions: Listen and join in.

E as in field.
E as in money.
E as in sunny, bunny,
and funny.

Long e

y   ey

ie

Blend It

Directions: Chorally read the words.

INTRODUCE

1. piece	niece	field	shield	brief	chief
2. funny	happy	sunny	silly	tricky	sleepy
3. key	monkey	money	honey	valley	turkey

4. I am happy at school.

5. The monkey can do a funny trick.

REVIEW

6. pie	goes	lies	toe	wild	find
7. told	careful	wearing	stairs	claws	talking

Daily Practice

Directions: Do one activity each day. Then check the box.

☐ Build Fluency Read the words each day by yourself and to a partner.

☐ Mark It Circle all the words with ey. Underline all the words with long e spelled ie.

☐ Spell It Have a partner say each word. Write the word. Check your answer.

☐ Write About It Use the words to create a story. Draw a box around the words from the list that you used.

Read-Spell-Write

Directions: Write each word two times. Say each letter as you write it.

1. also _____

2. myself _____

3. off _____

4. seven _____

Use in Context

Directions: Complete each sentence with a word from above.
Read the finished sentences to a partner.

1. The _____ monkeys are so silly.

2. The key fell _____ the desk.

3. We _____ play ball in the field.

4. I can count the money by _____.

Connected Text

Directions: **Read the "how-to" list. Then answer the questions.**

How to Have Fun at the Zoo

Here are some ways to have
fun at the zoo.

- Look at the zoo map. Use
  the key to find the animals.
- There is a farm at the zoo. You can see
  turkeys and a donkey.
- Check out the goats. There are seven of them!
- Feeding time at the zoo is also fun. The seals
  clap for pieces of fish.
- Save the monkeys for last. They are funny and
  noisy. They even shriek!
- Don't forget to make a brief stop for a snack.
  It is a busy day.

Interact with the Text

Directions: **Mark the text.**

1. Circle all the words with long e spelled ey.

2. Draw a box around the words with long e spelled ie.

Directions: **Write about the text.**

3. What do the seals do for pieces of fish? Tell a partner. Then write about it.

_____

- -

_____

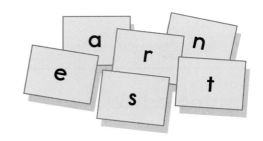

Word Sort

Sort It Out

Directions: Read each word. Then sort the words.
Write each word in the correct box.

brief   chief   field   funny   happy

key   money   monkey   piece   silly

y

ey

ie

What did you learn about how words work?

_____

- -

_____

_____

Think and Write

Directions: Listen to each picture name.
Write the spelling for each sound in a separate box.

1.

2.

3.

Listen and Spell

Directions: Write each word and sentence that you hear.

1. _____ 2. _____

3. _____ 4. _____

5. _____

Make New Words

Directions: Make words with the letter cards on page 448.
Write the words on the lines.

_____   _____

- - - - - - - - - - - - - - - - -   - - - - - - - - - - - - - - - - -

_____   _____

- - - - - - - - - - - - - - - - -   - - - - - - - - - - - - - - - - -

_____   _____

- - - - - - - - - - - - - - - - -   - - - - - - - - - - - - - - - - -

_____   _____

- - - - - - - - - - - - - - - - -   - - - - - - - - - - - - - - - - -

_____   _____

- - - - - - - - - - - - - - - - -   - - - - - - - - - - - - - - - - -

_____   _____

- - - - - - - - - - - - - - - - -   - - - - - - - - - - - - - - - - -

_____   _____

- - - - - - - - - - - - - - - - -   - - - - - - - - - - - - - - - - -

_____   _____

Name _____

My Super Silly Story

—1—

I like to tell stories.

Funny stories. Silly stories.

Stories to make you laugh.

I always laugh myself, too.

I know. This story is too silly!

You tell me a story.

Make it super silly. I like to laugh.

—4—

2

Once there was a monkey
that made keys for money.
His friend was a turkey.
It's tricky for a turkey to
make keys. No fingers!

— Fold —

The monkey also made cakes.
The turkey was so happy.
Instead of one piece of
cake, the monkey gave
him seven!

3

432 Long e • Lesson 30

Transition to Longer Words

Directions: Choose a syllable from each box to make a word. Then write the word.

fox	fun	mon	near	peace

es	ful	key	ly	ny

1. _____ + _____ = _____

2. _____ + _____ = _____

3. _____ + _____ = _____

4. _____ + _____ = _____

5. _____ + _____ = _____

Directions: Write a sentence using a word you wrote.

6. _____

Read and Write

Directions: Say each picture name. Circle the word for the picture.
Write it on the line.

---

free

keep

key

1. _____

---

fifty

thirty

twenty

2. _____

---

honey

piece

pony

3. _____

---

baby

brief

thief

4. _____

---

candy

chief

city

5. _____

---

money

monkey

valley

6. _____

Build Fluency

Directions: Complete each sentence. Use at least one word
with y, ey, or ie.

1. I see seven _____.

2. We also _____.

3. Get off _____.

4. Today is _____.

Directions: Write a sentence using each word pair.

5. | key, told | _____

6. | piece, share | _____

Word Ladder

Directions: Listen to each clue. Then write the word.
Start at the bottom and climb to the top.

Bees make this in their hives.
Change one letter.

_____

You use this to buy things.
Take away one letter.

_____

This animal swings from tree to tree.
Change one letter.

_____

This animal is like a horse but is smaller.
Add three letters.

_____

What you use to unlock a door
Take away three letters.

_____

Start → t u r k e y

Write About It

Directions: Read "My Super Silly Story" again.
Write what you learned about the monkey and the turkey.

Fluency Check

Directions: Listen to the child read the word list. Mark one check in the green box if the word is read correctly (accuracy). Mark another check in the blue box if it is read automatically (fluency).

CUMULATIVE ASSESSMENT

Lesson	Word			Lesson	Word		
30	happy	☐	☐	**27**	care	☐	☐
	monkey	☐	☐		upstairs	☐	☐
	piece	☐	☐		share	☐	☐
	chief	☐	☐		bear	☐	☐
29	pie	☐	☐	**26**	dawn	☐	☐
	fried	☐	☐		talking	☐	☐
	goes	☐	☐		salt	☐	☐
	tiptoe	☐	☐		hallway	☐	☐
28	child	☐	☐	**25**	toys	☐	☐
	kind	☐	☐		broil	☐	☐
	sold	☐	☐		coin	☐	☐
	golden	☐	☐		enjoy	☐	☐

Number Correct (accuracy): _____ /24

Number Automatic (fluency): _____ /24

Lesson 6	Lesson 5	Lesson 4	Lesson 3	Lesson 2	Lesson 1
black	bell	bug	dot	big	bat
block	get	bun	got	dig	can
clap	let	cut	hop	fit	cat
class	men	dug	hot	hit	fan
clock	net	fun	lot	lip	fat
club	pen	hug	mop	pig	hat
flag	sell	nut	not	rip	man
flat	tell	rug	pop	sit	pan
flip	ten	run	pot	wig	ran
flop	wet	sun	top	zip	sat

Lesson 1	Lesson 2	Lesson 3	Lesson 4	Lesson 5	Lesson 6
a	a	a	a	a	a
m	b	d	b	b	b
n	d	h	d	d	c
p	h	i	f	e	f
r	i	l	g	g	i
s	l	m	i	i	ck
t	m	o	n	l	l
	s	p	r	r	p
	t	t	s	s	s
			u	t	

Lesson 12	Lesson 11	Lesson 10	Lesson 9	Lesson 8	Lesson 7
bit	bank	catch	fish	crab	slap
bite	king	check	path	crib	sled
can	long	chin	ship	dress	slip
cane	pink	chop	shop	drip	snap
cap	ring	itch	shut	drop	sniff
cape	sing	match	thick	grab	snug
hate	sink	what	this	grass	stem
hid	strong	when	trash	grin	stick
hide	thank	where	wish	trap	stop
this	think	which	with	trick	stuff

Lesson 7	Lesson 8	Lesson 9	Lesson 10	Lesson 11	Lesson 12
ck	a	d	a	a	a
i	b	f	c	b	b
k	c	h	ck	g	c
l	ck	i	e	h	d
ll	d	o	h	i	e
n	g	p	i	k	i
o	i	s	n	n	k
p	p	w	o	s	l
s	r		p	t	m
t	t		t	u	t

Lesson 18	Lesson 17	Lesson 16	Lesson 15	Lesson 14	Lesson 13
bright	boat	clean	gray	go	bone
cry	coach	meat	may	got	cube
fight	coat	need	nail	hi	cute
fly	grow	peach	paint	hit	home
might	know	queen	play	me	hope
my	low	seed	rain	men	Steve
night	road	sleep	sail	no	these
right	show	speak	say	not	those
shy	snow	tea	stay	she	use
try	toast	week	train	shell	vote

Lesson 13	Lesson 14	Lesson 15	Lesson 16	Lesson 17	Lesson 18
e	e	a	a	a	c
h	g	i	b	b	e
i	h	l	d	c	f
l	i	m	e	g	h
m	m	n	ee	n	l
o	n	p	f	o	m
p	o	r	m	r	r
u	s	s	n	t	s
	t	t	s	w	t
	w	y	t		y

Lesson 24	Lesson 23	Lesson 22	Lesson 21	Lesson 20	Lesson 19
brown	boot	corn	bird	arm	argue
count	brook	fork	burn	art	bug
cow	cook	more	dirt	bark	cue
down	goose	oar	first	farm	few
found	hoot	roar	girl	harm	menu
house	noon	score	her	mark	music
how	shook	short	hurt	park	nut
loud	soon	soar	stir	shark	shut
now	stood	store	turn	smart	stuck
sound	wood	storm	verb	start	value

Lesson 19	Lesson 20	Lesson 21	Lesson 22	Lesson 23	Lesson 24
b	a	b	c	b	d
c	c	c	e	c	e
e	d	f	f	d	h
f	f	h	h	g	m
m	h	l	m	h	n
s	k	n	o	k	o
t	m	r	p	l	p
u	p	t	r	oo	s
	r	u	s	r	th
	t		t	s	u

446 Letter Cards

Lesson 30	Lesson 29	Lesson 28	Lesson 27	Lesson 26	Lesson 25
brief	cried	blind	bear	ball	boil
chief	die	child	care	call	boy
field	doe	cold	chair	chalk	broil
funny	dried	find	dare	fall	coin
happy	goes	fold	fair	halt	join
key	Joe	kind	hair	salt	joy
money	pie	mild	pair	small	noise
monkey	tie	sold	pear	talk	oil
piece	toe	told	stare	tall	soil
silly	tried	wild	wear	walk	toy

Lesson 25	Lesson 26	Lesson 27	Lesson 28	Lesson 29	Lesson 30
b	a	air	d	c	e
c	b	are	f	d	h
i	c	b	i	e	k
j	k	c	l	g	m
l	l	ear	m	i	n
n	l	h	n	o	o
o	m	p	o	p	y
s	s	s	s	r	
t	t	t	t	s	
y	w	w	w	t	